the 30 day
WHOLE FOOD

WEIGHT LOSS
CHALLENGE

WHOLE
FOOD

30 DAY

THE 30 DAY WHOLE FOOD WEIGHT LOSS CHALLENGE
30 DAY WHOLE FOOD: THREE WHOLE RECIPES COOKED IN LESS THEN 30 MINUTES
30 DAY WEIGHT LOSS EXERCISE PLAN INCLUDED

D1225969

Katie Banks

Contents

A whole new life starts here

Are you committed to maintain a healthy lifestyle that keeps you fit and disease-free?

The most important thing that needs to be changed is your diet and the food you eat. Incorporate a healthy diet of whole foods and sum it up with a daily exercise routine- the results will start showing instantly. You work out the right way, with the right diet – and it's just a matter of time for the results to show.

Oh wait, are you saying you are too busy?

Don't worry, we know you're - you just need to devote maximum of an hour each day for something as vital as your health. This book brings you a 30 day meal plan with whole food recipes coupled with a complete list of exercises aimed to increase your strength and vitality.

What will you find in this plan to help you achieving your goals?

· 30 Days, 3 delicious recipes each day including breakfast, lunch and dinner.

· All ingredients are whole food, closest to their natural state which means more nutrients, vitamins and minerals.

· You can cook all three meals every day within 30 minutes.

· A 30 day Schdeule of exercises to be performed in less than 30 minutes.

Eat right and workout the right way to maximize the benefits!

Day One

Day One starts with a hearty and refreshing breakfast that calls for oat fritters with mint. The meal is packed with both complex and simple carbs, unsaturated fats, and a fine portion of proteins to help you start the day with a sufficient boost of energy. After that, you're going to please your taste buds with a slightly oriental lunch – the Chicken and Tomato Buckwheat. It will help you get through even the most intensive day at work. It's rich in proteins, packed with vitamins, and its juicy flavours will surely dance around your palate to remind you of what a healthy lunch is about. Finally, you the Feta Cheese Salad will provide you with unquestionable nutritional values that ensure proper regeneration during your sleep. Most importantly, you can prepare each of these whole-food meals in under 15 minutes.

Chicken and Tomato Buckwheat

Oat Fritters With Mint

 4   90   7'

1. Place oat flakes, linseed, banana, soy milk, and dates in a food processor. Mix until fully combined, 2-3 minutes.
2. Grease a frying pan with the canola oil. Fry the fritters on both sides until golden.
3. Serve with fresh mint on top.

-45g oat flakes (1.6 oz)	-½ ripe banana	-2 dried dates
-1 tbsp. linseed	-60ml soy milk (2.0 fl oz)	-2 tsp. canola oil for frying

Chicken and Tomato Buckwheat

 2   366   15'

1. Bring salted water in a medium pot to a boil. Add the buckwheat and cook it for 15 minutes on low heat.
2. In the meantime, heat the oil in a large pan. Add the chopped onion and saute it for 2-3 minutes.
3. Add garlic and fry it for 1 minute, until fragrant.
4. Add the chicken and pour in the tomato sauce. Add corn kernels, basil, oregano, salt and pepper, and cook for 10 minutes on medium heat.

-200g buckwheat (7.0 oz)	-300g tomato puree (10.6 oz)	-½ tsp. dried oregano
-150g chicken breast, cut into small bite-sized -chunks (5.3 oz)	-2 small garlic cloves, minced	-1 tsp. Himalayan salt
	-1 tsp. sweet paprika	-½ tsp. freshly ground black pepper
-1 large onion, diced	-1 tsp. hot paprika	-1 tbsp. canola oil for frying
-4 tbsp. corn kernels	-1 tsp. dried basil	

Feta Cheese Salad

 4   254   8'

1. Carefully wash the lettuce and dry it on paper towels. Shred the lettuce into small pieces and place it in a bowl.
2. Add cherry tomatoes, feta cheese, and corn kernels.
3. Deseed and dice the chili.
4. Add the chili and the onion to the bowl with the salad.
5. Season with salt and pepper.
6. Mix all ingredients of the vinaigrette dressing.
7. Pour the vinaigrette over the salad.

For the salad:		**For the vinaigrette dressing:**
-1/3 lettuce	-170g corn kernels (6.0 oz)	-4tbsp. olive oil
-300g cherry tomatoes, cut in halves (10.6 oz)	-½ red chili	-1 tbsp. lime juice
-100g feta cheese, crumbled (3.5 oz)	-¼ red onion	-½ tbsp. honey
		-Salt and pepper to taste

Day 2

Welcome to the second day of your adventure with simple whole-food recipes. Today, we will greet the morning with a Sweet Spinach Power Cocktail that is rich in calcium, fibre, and protein. The main course is about to show you that whole-wheat pasta is actually what your hidden dreams are made of. It's accompanied by the lactose-free goat cheese and a red bell pepper – everything garnished with fresh basil leaves, sea salt and, of course, freshly ground black pepper. Since we want to cut down on carbohydrates when the end of the day draws near, your belly will appreciate the hearty and crunchy Avocado Paste and Poached Egg Bruschettas. Seems like a day full of flavours and nutrients, doesn't it? Let's get healthy!

Avocado Paste and Poached Egg Bruschettas

Sweet Spinach Power Cocktail 2 300 2'

1. Place all ingredients in a food processor or a blender.
2. Mix them until smooth.
3. Pour the cocktail into glasses and drink immediately.

-120g fresh raw spinach (4.2 oz)

-2 ripe pears, peeled, deseeded, and diced

-140g grapes (4.9 oz)

-340ml natural yoghurt (11.5 fl oz)

-4 tbsp. finely chopped ripe avocado

-4 tbsp. lime juice

Goat Cheese and Pepper Pasta 2 350 12-15'

1. Cook the pasta according to the package directions and drain it.
2. Heat the olive oil and butter in a medium pan over medium heat.
3. Add the onion, red bell pepper, and garlic. Season with salt and cook on medium heat for 12-15 minutes, stirring from time to time. The pepper should be tender by that time. Finally, add black olives.
4. Reduce heat to low and stir in the drained pasta. Continue cooking for additional 2 minutes.
5. Remove from the heat, add the goat cheese, and basil.
6. Season with salt and pepper
7. Mix well and serve immediately.

-2 tbsp. extra virgin olive oil

-1 tbsp. unsalted butter

-1 small onion, diced

-1 ½ red bell pepper, diced

-2 garlic cloves, minced

-8 black olives, sliced

-150g whole-wheat 'penne' pasta (5.3 oz)

-70g goat cheese, crumbled (2.5 oz)

-A handful of fresh basil leaves

-Sea salt and freshly ground black pepper to taste

Avocado Paste and Poached Egg Bruschettas 2 320 10'

1. Toast the bread in a grill pan. Rub it with the garlic and sprinkle several drops of olive oil over each slice.
2. Wash, peel and deseed avocado. Squash it with a fork and season with salt and pepper.
3. Boil 750ml (25.4 fl oz) of salted water in a medium pot. Use the handle of a spatula or spoon to quickly stir the water in one direction until a whirlpool forms. Drop the egg into the centre of the whirlpool and cook it for 3-4 minutes. Repeat the same with the other egg.
4. Cut the cherry tomatoes in half, season with salt and pepper, and garnish with the chopped onion.
5. Spread the avocado paste over the toasted bread. Place the poached egg on top and season it with additional salt, pepper, and chili flakes.

-2 slices of whole-wheat bread

-½ garlic clove

-2 tsp. extra virgin olive oil

-1 ripe avocado

-2 eggs

-150g cherry tomatoes (5.3 oz)

-1 small red onion, finely chopped

-A pinch of each: salt, pepper, chili

-flakes, dried basil

Day 3

Your meal plan for today includes Goat Cheese & Tomato Grilled Sandwich, which is a delicious and healthy way to start the day. After that, you're going to enjoy a light salad full of veggies, such as avocado, red bell peppers, and tomatoes. Should the day start coming to an end – it's smoothie time! But it's not just another bland drink to ingest in the evening. It's Kale & Ginger Smoothie, a drink full of green and healing power. Let's go!

Millet Salad With Avocado, Red Bell Pepper & Tomatoes

Goat Cheese & Tomato Grilled Sandwich 2 225 5'

1. Cut the baguette in half, carve out the flesh, and flatten the bread with your hands.
2. In a small bowl, combine all ingredients of the Za'atar spice mix.
3. Drizzle some olive oil on the surface of the baguette and sprinkle it with the Za'atar spice mix.
4. On one half of the baguette, place the goat cheese slices, tomato, and several rocket leaves. Add salt to taste.
5. Fold the sandwich and grill it in a toaster or a grill until the bread is golden-brown.

-1 whole-grain baguette

-Several drops of extra virgin olive oil

-100g goat cheese (3.5 oz)

-1 tomato

-Rocket lettuce for serving

Za'atar spice mix:

-1 tbsp. dried thyme

-1 ½ tsp. toasted sesame seeds

-Pinch of salt and pepper

-One pinch of each: dried oregano, dried parsley, cumin, marjoram

Millet Salad With Avocado, Red Bell Pepper & Tomatoes 2 330 15'

1. Toast the millet in a medium saucepan for 2-3 minutes, whisking from time to time.
2. Pour in 125ml (4.2 fl oz) water, add salt and pepper to taste, and pour in 1 tbsp. olive oil. Cover the saucepan and cook the millet for about 10 minutes until soft.
3. Open the saucepan, place the millet on plates, and cool to room temperature.
4. Peel and dice the avocado, and drizzle it with a juice from 1 lemon. Dice the red bell pepper and cut the tomatoes in halves.
5. Combine the millet with lettuce leaves, avocado, red bell pepper, and tomatoes.
6. Serve the salad on plates, place fried eggs on top, and sprinkle with sunflower seed kernels.

-50g millet (1.8 oz)

-A handful of lettuce

-1 avocado

-150g red bell pepper (5.3 oz)

-200g cherry tomatoes (7.0 oz)

-2 eggs (fried)

-2 tbsp. sunflower seed kernels

-Salt, pepper, extra virgin olive oil, and lemon juice to taste

Ginger & Kale Smoothie 1 158 85'

1. Wash the kale and separate the soft leaves from the central part.
2. Place the kale leaves to the blender. Peel and slice the ginger, and add it to the kale.
3. Pour in the orange juice and add the peeled banana. Mix until the beverage is perfectly smooth.

-30g fresh kale (1.0 oz)

-½ cm fresh ginger

-250ml orange juice (8.5 fl oz)

-¼ banana

Day 4

Day 4 is full of extraordinary flavors that will take your eating experience to a whole new level. For breakfast, you'll have Smoked Salmon & Guacamole Crostini so that you can revel in freshly baked slices of bread topped with fish and avocado paste. The lunch will consist of Tuna & Cherry Tomatoes Pasta – a super-quick meal with a generous portion of protein, healthy fats, and complex carbs. In the end, both your taste buds and tummy are going to experience an unusual dish - Chorizo & Kale Stew. Are you ready for a dash of diversity on your plates?

Tuna & Cherry Tomatoes Pasta

Smoked Salmon & Guacamole Crostini 2 383 7'

1. Cut the baguette in half and toast it in a pan until golden-brown. Peel the garlic and cut it in half. Rub the baguette with one half of the clove and save another piece for the guacamole
2. For the guacamole: cut the avocado in half lengthwise and remove the seed. Take out the flesh with a spoon, dice it, and place the avocado in a bowl. Grate another half of the garlic clove and add it to the avocado. Drizzle with 1 teaspoon of lemon juice and 1 teaspoon of olive oil. Season with salt and pepper. Mix well and smash with a fork.
3. For the mayo sauce: combine mayonnaise with sour cream, 1 teaspoon of lemon juice, and ¼ grated garlic clove. Season with salt and pepper. Add the chopped dill and mix all ingredients together.
4. Coat your baguette slices with the guacamole. Add chunks of smoked salmon and drizzle it with lemon juice. Season with freshly ground pepper. Top each slice with 1 teaspoon of the mayo sauce.

-½ whole-grain baguette

-100g smoked salmon (3.5 oz)

-1 avocado

-1 garlic clove

-2 tsp. lemon juice + more to taste

-1 tsp. olive oil

-1 tsp. chopped dill

-2 tbsp. mayonnaise

-1 tbsp. sour cream

-Salt to taste

Tuna & Cherry Tomatoes Pasta 2 377 15'

1. Cook the pasta until al dente, about 4-5 minutes. Drain the pasta and save a couple tablespoons of water from the pot – you can pour it into a glass and set aside.
2. Melt the olive oil and butter in the pot in which you cooked the pasta. Add the sliced garlic and sauté for about 1-2 minutes, stirring from time to time. Pour in the wine and cook for 2 more minutes until a half of the liquid evaporates.
3. Add 2 tablespoons of oil from the can with tuna. Slice the tomatoes, add them to the pot and cook for about 2 minutes, stirring constantly until the tomatoes are soft.
4. Stir in the cooked pasta along with the saved water and bring the pot to a boil.
5. Remove from the heat and add the tuna chunks.
6. Serve the pasta on plates and top it with sliced olives, parmesan, and basil.

-150g whole-wheat casarecce pasta (5.3 oz)

-1 tbsp. extra virgin olive oil

-2 small garlic cloves

-2 tbsp. soft unsalted butter

-60ml white wine (2.0 fl oz)

-100g tuna in oil (3.5 oz)

-150g cherry tomatoes (5.3 oz)

-5 black olives

-Freshly grated parmesan and fresh basil leaves for garnish

Chorizo and Kale Stew 4 254   8'

1. Cut off the hard stems of the kale. Bring water in a pot to a boil. Cook the kale for 3-4 minutes and drain it. Set aside.
2. In a medium pan, cook the chorizo and onion on medium heat for 7 minutes, stirring constantly until the onion is soft and the chorizo is drowned.
3. Stir in the canned tomatoes and cook for 5 minutes.
4. Stir in the kale and cook on high heat for about 1 minute.
5. Season with freshly ground pepper.

-200g kale, rinsed and chopped (7.0 oz)

-1 large onion, diced.

-80g chorizo sausage, the outer layer peeled off (2.8 oz)

-200g canned tomatoes, diced (7.0 oz)

Day 5

You know what they say – a bowl of oatmeal a day keeps the doctor away. That's why the Chia Seed Oatmeal is your first meal on Day 5 of out 30-day plan with whole-foods dishes. The lunch, on the other hand, will take you on a journey to India thanks to the flavourful Chicken Curry with Beans and Tomatoes. After you're don with your day-to-day struggles at work, there are some Turkey Burgers to provide you with whole proteins which will take care of your regeneration during sleep.

Chicken Curry with Beans and Tomatoes+

Chia Seed Oatmeal
 2 400 5'

1. Add oat flakes and chia seeds to a small pot. Pour in the milk and bring to a boil. Cook the oatmeal for 5 minutes.
2. In the meantime, prepare the fruit salsa. Roughly chop the strawberries and place them in a bowl. Add pomegranate seeds, drizzle with lemon juice, and sweeten with honey. Combine all ingredients together.
3. Pour the oatmeal into large place and top with the fruit salsa. Serve immediately.

-90g instant oat flakes (3.2 oz)

-1 tbsp. chia seeds

-500ml whole milk (16.9 fl oz)

-250g strawberries (8.8 fl oz)

-¼ pomegranate

-1 tbsp. lemon juice

-1 tsp. honey

Chicken Curry with Beans and Tomatoes
 2 577 17'

1. Cook the rice according to the package directions.
2. While the rice is cooking, prepare the curry. Dice the chicken breast and season it with salt, coriander, turmeric, chili powder, and combine the seasoned meat with 1 tablespoon of coconut oil.
3. Grate the ginger, garlic, and onion. Add 1-2 tablespoons of water and mix until well combined. Heat the second tablespoon of coconut oil. Add the ginger-garlic paste and sauté for a while.
4. Add the diced chicken and sauté for about 5 minutes, stirring from time to time. Pour in ½ cup of water and bring to a boil.
5. Pour in the coconut milk and cook for about 10 minutes. Add the canned beans, peeled and diced tomatoes, and cook for another 5 minutes.
6. Add mustard, lime juice, and sugar. Boil for another 1-2 minutes. Season with salt to taste.
7. Serve with the cooked rice and fresh cilantro leaves.

-½ boneless skinless chicken breast

-½ tsp. ground coriander

-1 tsp. ground turmeric

-½ tsp. chili powder

-2 tbsp. coconut oil

-½ onion

-3-cm root of fresh ginger

-1 can of beans

-200ml coconut milk (7.0 fl oz)

-1 tomato

-1 tsp. French mustard

-2 tsp. lime juice

-1 tsp. brown sugar

Turkey Burgers
 6 196 8'

1. In a large bowl, combine the ground turkey with chopped dried tomatoes. Add the water, olive oil, all spices, and the amaranth flour. Knead by hand for 1 minute.
2. Form 6 flat patties, (each 1,5 cm thick) and coat them in the olive oil.
3. Heat the grill pan over medium heat and fry the burgers for 5 minutes per side.

-500g ground turkey (17.6 oz)

-4 tbsp. cold water

-4 dried tomatoes, chopped

-80g amaranth flour (2.8 oz)

-1 tbsp. olive oil from the dried tomatoes

-1 tsp. ground coriander

-1 tsp. sweet smoked paprika

-½ tsp. hot paprika

-1 tsp. ground turmeric

-½ tsp. dried oregano

-1 cup natural yoghurt for serving

Day 6

Today we'll focus mostly on veggies and cheese. Our menu consists of a Fig & Ricotta Sandwich, Avocado, Mozzarella & Tomato Salad, and Fried Broccoli 'Rice'. I bet you're wondering why we put rice in inverted comas. Well, see for yourself what is so fascinating about the last meal! But first, indulge yourself in a flavourful breakfast sandwich and a creamy, juicy lunch salad.

Fried Broccoli Rice

Fig & Ricotta Sandwich

 4 217 5'

1. Lightly toast the pine nuts in a medium pan – it should take about 2-3 minutes on low heat.
2. Slice each bun in half and toast each piece in a dry pan. Spread butter on each bun, then add ricotta, sliced figs, and sprinkle your sandwiches with the pine nuts.

-100g ricotta cheese (3.5 oz)

-2 fresh figs, sliced

-3 tbsp. pine nuts

-2 spelt buns

-Unsalted butter for spreading

Avocado, Mozzarella & Tomato Salad

 2 606 5'

1. Mix all ingredients of the salad. Season with salt and pepper to taste.
2. In a small bowl, combine all ingredients of the vinaigrette sauce. Add lightly toasted pine nuts and pour the vinaigrette over the salad.
3. Serve with the toasted bread.

-100g rocket lettuce, rinsed (3.5 oz)

-1 avocado, sliced

-100g cherry tomatoes, cut in halves (3.5 oz)

-125g mozzarella cheese, sliced (4.4 oz)

-4 tbsp. pine nuts

-Vinaigrette: 3 tbsp. extra virgin olive oil, salt and pepper to taste, ½ tsp.

-Dijon mustard, 1 tsp. lemon

-juice, ½ garlic clove (grated)

-2 slices of whole-wheat bread.

Fried Broccoli "Rice"

 2 320 15'

1. Break the broccoli into smaller chunks and shred them in a food processor into very tiny pieces.
2. Grate the garlic and finely chop the onion.
3. Heat the oil in a large pan over medium heat. Add the onion, garlic, pumpkin seeds, chopped cashews, and sauté everything for about 5 minutes, stirring from time to time until all ingredients are lightly browned.
4. Add the cranberries, broccoli, and all spices. Stir everything carefully and cook for about 5-7 minutes. Remove from the heat.
5. Sprinkle with chives and drizzle with lemon juice.
6. Top with fried eggs (pan-fry the eggs for 2-3 minutes until the white is coagulated and the yolk is runny).

-300g broccoli (10.6 oz)

-1 garlic clove

-¼ onion

-2 tbsp. canola oil

-2 tbsp. pumpkin seeds

-2tbsp. cashew nuts

-1 tbsp. dried cranberries

-½ tsp each: ground turmeric, sweet paprika, hot paprika, dried oregano

-Salt and pepper, to taste

-A handful of chives, finely chopped

-1 tbsp. lemon juice

-2 fried eggs for serving

Day 7

Surprisingly, some people still think of healthy food as bland and monotonous. Today, we're going to prove that they are all wrong about their prejudice toward whole-foods recipes. Although the breakfast - Egg & Feta Cheese Paste - may sound a bit modest, the other meals will rock today's plan. For lunch, you'll provide your palate with a pleasant experience by eating Fried Chili & Garlic Shrimps, and the dinner will make you feel delighted by the Asian flavours of the Chicken Chow Mein Noodles.

Egg & Feta Cheese Paste

Egg & Feta Cheese Paste

   2   253   10'

1. Hard boil the eggs: place them in a boiling water and cook for about 8-10 minutes over medium heat.
2. Peel the eggs and dice them. Combine the eggs with the feta cheese, add mayonnaise, chives, and season with salt and freshly ground pepper. Mix everything well, place the paste in a bowl and decorate with the remaining chives.

-3 large eggs

-100g feta cheese, diced

-1 tbsp. mayonnaise

-1 tbsp. finely chopped chives

Fried Chili & Garlic Shrimps

   2   370   8'

1. Place the frozen shrimps in a large bowl and cover them with lukewarm water until defrosted. Rinse the shrimps and dry them on paper towels.
2. Heat half of the butter in a pan and add the garlic and chili. Sauté for 30 seconds. Add shrimps and cook for 1 minute on one side.
3. Pour in the wine and let it evaporate on high heat. Reduce heat to medium, flip the shrimps and cook for another minute.
4. Flip the shrimps again so that the cut touches the pan and cook them for 30 more seconds.
5. Add chopped parsley, the remaining butter, and olive oil. Melt the butter and turn off the heat.
6. Season with salt and a squeeze of lemon juice.

-250g frozen shrimps (8.8 oz)

-4 garlic cloves

-40g unsalted butter (1.4 oz)

-50ml white wine (optional) (1.7 fl oz)

-3 tbsp. extra virgin olive oil

-Sea salt to taste

-½ chili pepper, finely chopped

-A small handful of fresh parsley, finely chopped

Egg & Feta Cheese

    2   383   12'

1. Cook the noodles in boiling water for about 2-3 minutes and rinse it with cold water.
2. Dice the chicken into 1,5-cm chunks.
3. Heat the canola oil in wok. Add garlic and sauté for 30 seconds. Add the chicken breast and sauté for another 1,5 -2 minutes.
4. Add the carrot and the remaining vegetables. Stir-fry for 2 minutes.
5. Stir in the cooked noodles. Season with white pepper, sugar, sesame oil and soy sauce. Mix well and stir-fry for 1-2 minutes.

-2 tbsp. canola oil

-2 garlic cloves

-250g boneless, skinless chicken breast (8.8 oz)

-½ carrot, cut lengthwise in stripes

-10 pea pods, cut lengthwise in stripes

-½ red bell pepper, cut lengthwise in stripes

-2 green onions, sliced

-100g Mie noodles (3.5 oz)

-¼ tsp. white pepper

-½ tsp. brown sugar

-1 tsp. sesame oil

-3 tbsp. light soy sauce

Day 8

Today, we'll introduce you to a gluten-free breakfast (pancakes) so that you can see that gluten-free meals are also juicy and full of flavor. During the lunch break, you'll be accompanied by Smoked Salmon Sandwiches served with fresh dill and a drizzle of lemon juice. Finally, we'll end the day with some Honey-covered Walnut Sandwiches to add some sweetness to your evening.

Gluten-free Pancakes

Goat Cheese & Tomato Grilled Sandwich 2 542 15'

1. In a large bowl, combine yoghurt with eggs and melted coconut oil. Mix the ground almonds with rice flour and baking soda, and add the mixture into the bowl with the pancake batter.
2. Heat a large non-stick pan (don't add any oil). Grab 1 tablespoon of the pancake batter and put it in the pan. Fry 3-4 pancakes simultaneously on a medium heat for about 1,5-2 minutes per side. Flip the pancakes and fry for another 2 minutes.
3. Drizzle the pancakes with orange juice.

-300g natural yoghurt (10.6 oz)

-1 tbsp. maple syrup

-2 eggs, lightly beaten

-3 tbsp. melted coconut oil

-60g ground almonds (2.1 oz)

-75g rice flour (2.5 oz)

-1 ½ tsp. baking soda

-Orange juice for serving

Smoked Salmon Sandwiches 2 339 5'

1. Spread the cream cheese over the bread, lay the salmon and sprinkle with the chopped dill.
2. Drizzle with lemon juice.

-200g smoked salmon (7.0 oz)

-100g cream cheese (3.5 oz)

-4 slices whole-wheat bread

-Fresh dill, finely chopped

-Juice from ½ lemon to drizzle

Honey-covered Walnut Sandwiches 2 550 5'

1. Finely chop the walnuts and lightly toast them on a dry pan over low heat – it should take 2-3 minutes.
2. Combine the nuts with honey.
3. Toast the bread on a pan or in the oven.
4. Spread the honey-walnut batter over the slices while the bread is still hot.

-4 slices of rye bread

-8 tbsp. honey

-20 walnuts

Day 9

Have you ever heard of a 3-meal plan that can be prepared in 20 minutes? Well, it's right here! Time to get energized with the Young Barley Smoothie for breakfast, followed by the Chicken Thai soup – an Asian dish full of vegetables and flavourful broth to keep you strong and full of vitamins during the day. The evening will be accompanied by the Greek Salad served in a fancy way. Off we go!

Young Barley Smoothie

Young Barley Smoothie

 2   255   3'

1. In a blender or a food processor, combine the mango, banana, apple juice, and yoghurt.
2. Add the barley.
3. Mix well and pour the smoothie into glasses.

-1 mango, peeled, deseeded, and diced

-1 banana, peeled and diced

-125g Greek yoghurt

-350ml apple juice

-2-4 tsp. young barley

Chicken Thai Soup

 4   401   15'

1. Place the noodles in a pot, cover with cold water, and soak the noodles for 10-15 minutes.
2. In the meantime, heat the oil in a separate pot over medium heat. Add the curry paste and sauté for 1 minute. Add the diced chicken and sauté for about 3 minutes, stirring constantly.
3. Add the onion and sauté for another 2 minutes. After that, place the pepper and sauté again for about 2 minutes. Pour in the broth and bring to a boil.
4. Add the mushrooms, noodles, and corn kernels. Cook the soup for about 5 minutes.
5. Stir in the fish sauce and coconut milk.
6. Remove from the heat and stir in the chives. Drizzle with lime juice.
7. Garnish with fresh cilantro leaves and serve immediately.

-25g Vermicelli rice noodles (0.9 oz)

-2 tsp. coconut oil

-2 tsp. Thai curry paste (green or red)

-250g boneless, skinless chicken breast (8.8 oz)

-½ onion, finely chopped

-½ red bell pepper, thinly sliced lengthwise

-1,5l vegetable or chicken broth, diced (50.7 fl oz)

-150g mushrooms, sliced (5.3 oz)

-5 tbsp. canned corn kernels

-250ml coconut milk (8.5 fl oz)

-2 tsp. fish sauce

-Chopped chives

-Juice from ½ lime

-Fresh cilantro leaves for garnish

Greek Salad

 1   550   7'

1. For the vinaigrette: in a small bowl, whisk together the lemon juice with a pinch of salt until the salt dissolves. Gradually add the olive oil whisking constantly until well combined. Season with salt, pepper, and dried oregano.
2. Pour the vinaigrette into a jar. Add the cucumber, tomatoes, red onion, and olives.
3. Seal the jar.

-1 cucumber, finely chopped

-¼ red onion, thinly sliced

-125g cherry tomatoes, cut in halves (4.4 oz)

-100g feta cheese (3.5 oz)

-10 black olives, sliced

Vinaigrette: (1 tbsp. lemon juice + 3 tbsp. olive oil + 1 tsp. dried oregano + salt and pepper to taste)

Day 10

If you're looking for an extraordinary way to add pizzazz to your oatmeal, you'll find this Peanut Butter & Banana Oatmeal more than exciting. The Salmon & Avocado Salad for lunch is both healthy and easy to prepare, and it's tahini dressing makes the meal outstandingly delicious. Should the evening be cold and foggy, the White Vegetables Chowder will keep you warm and filled with delicate flavours accompanied by the crispy bacon.

White Vegetables Chowder

Peanut Butter & Banana Oatmeal 2 485 10'

1. Bring the milk to a boil in a pot. Add oat flakes and cook them for about 5 minutes over medium heat.
2. Drizzle the sliced banana with lemon juice.
3. In a small bowl, combine all ingredients of the peanut butter sauce.
4. Pour the oatmeal into bowls. Add the banana, peanut butter sauce, and sprinkle with chopped walnuts.

-90g instant oat flakes (3.2 oz)
-500ml milk (16.9 fl oz)
-1 banana, peeled and sliced

-1 tbsp. lemon juice
-20g walnuts, finely chopped (0.7 oz)

Peanut butter sauce: (1 tbsp. peanut butter + 2 tbsp. maple syrup + 1 tbsp. lemon juice)

Salmon & Avocado Salad with Tahini Dressing 2 615 10'

1. In a bowl, combine all ingredients of the tahini dressing.
2. Peel the skin off the salmon and rinse the fillets with water. Drizzle the fish with lemon juice and season it with salt, pepper, cumin, coriander, and paprika. Rub the salmon fillets with olive oil.
3. Preheat a non-stick frying pan. Add the salmon fillets and cook them on medium-high heat, 5 minutes per side.
4. Place the lettuce mix on plates, followed by the sliced radish and the avocado drizzled with lemon juice. Top with the salmon and spoon the sauce over the salad.
5. Sprinkle the salad with toasted sesame seeds.

-300g salmon fillets (10.6 oz)
-1 package of lettuce mix
-50g radish, sliced (1.8 oz)
-1 ripe avocado, peeled, deseeded, and sliced
-2 tbsp. sesame seeds

Marinade: (1 tsp. olive oil + 1 tsp. lemon juice + ½ tsp. ground cumin + ½ tsp. ground coriander seeds + ½ tsp. hot paprika + salt and pepper to taste)

Tahini Dressing: (2 tsp. tahini paste + ½ tbsp. honey + 2 tbsp. olive oil + 1 tbsp. lemon juice + salt and pepper to taste)

White Vegetables Chowder 4 350 15'

1. In a large pot, melt butter and add the onion. Sauté it until soft. Add the grated garlic clove along with the leek.
2. Add the parsley root, celery, potato and cauliflower florets. Cook for about 1-2 minutes, stirring constantly.
3. Add the chickpea with the brines. Pour in the hot broth and season the soup with salt, pepper, ginger, and nutmeg. Bring the soup to a boil over high heat. Reduce the heat, cover the pot with a lid and cook until vegetables are soft for about 13 minutes.
4. At the end, add milk and whipping cream, and mix the soup with an immersion blender until smooth.
5. Served with crispy bacon.

-30g unsalted butter (1.0 oz)
-1 onion, finely chopped
-1 garlic clove
-1 leek, only the white part, sliced
-½ celery root, diced
-2 parsley roots, sliced

-1 medium potato, diced
-300g frozen cauliflower, divided (10.6 oz)
-200g canned chickpea (7.0 oz)
-250ml milk (8.5 fl oz)
-125ml heavy cream (4.2 fl oz)

-3 white asparagus (optional)
-750ml vegetable broth (25.3 oz)
-1 tsp. grated ginger
-½ tsp. white pepper
-½ tsp. ground nutmeg

Day 11

Day 11 starts with the Smoothie Bowl full of mango, banana and natural yoghurt, topped with berries and nuts. For lunch, we'll take you to Italy with our Asparagus Pasta accompanied by ham and cheese. Finally, to cross the T's and dot the I's, we'll finish the day with a heart and tummy-warming Chicken Goulash. As always, the meals are healthy, quick, and super easy to prepare.

Chicken Goulash

Smoothie Bowl

 2   504   5'

1. Add the mango, banana, yoghurt, and apple juice to the blender. Mix well until perfectly smooth.
2. Pour the smoothie into bowls and garnish with fruits and nuts.

-2 mangos, peeled, deseeded, and diced

-2 bananas, peeled and sliced

-360g natural yoghurt (12.7 oz)

-250ml apple juice (8.5 fl oz)

30g (1.0 oz) each: raspberries, blueberries, walnuts, peaches, for serving

Asparagus Pasta with Ham and Cheese

 2   509   10'

1. Break off the hard parts of asparagus. Rinse the asparagus with water and cut them into 4-cm chunks.
2. In a large pot, bring water to a boil, add the pasta and cook until al dente (4-5 minutes).
3. In the meantime, heat 2 tablespoons of olive oil in a large non-stick pan. Add the garlic and sauté it for 1 minute. Stir in 1 tablespoon of olive oil, add asparagus, season with salt, and sauté again for 2 minutes. Add the chopped ham and cook for 30 more seconds. Season with fresh thyme and pepper, and stir well to combine.
4. Drain the pasta and add it to the pan. Add the chopped camembert and stir well until the cheese is melted. Drizzle with 1 tablespoon of olive oil and serve immediately.

-8 green asparagus

-100g whole-grain penne pasta (3.5 oz)

-4 garlic cloves

-4 tbsp. extra virgin olive oil

-150g camembert cheese (5.3 oz)

-80g prosciutto ham (2.8 oz)

-1 tbsp. fresh thyme

-Salt and freshly ground pepper to taste

Chicken Goulash

 2   476   15'

1. Heat the olive oil in a large non-stick pan. Add the onion and sauté it for 3 minutes over medium heat until softened. Stir in the grated garlic, red bell pepper, and sauté for 1 more minute.
2. Add the diced chicken breast and sauté it from each side for 2-3 minutes. Season the meat with salt and pepper, and add the butter, dried oregano, and sweet paprika.
3. Pour in the broth and tomato puree with the tomato paste. Stir well and bring to a boil.
4. Cook the goulash for about 2 minutes. You can add ½ teaspoon of the potato flour in order to thicken the sauce a bit.

-500g boneless, skinless chicken breast, diced (17.6 oz)

-2 tbsp. olive oil

-½ red bell pepper, deseeded and diced

-½ onion, finely chopped

-2 garlic cloves, finely chopped

-1 tsp. dried oregano

-½ tsp. sweet paprika

-60ml chicken or vegetable broth (2.0 fl oz)

-250ml tomato puree (8.5 fl oz)

-½ tbsp. unsalted butter

-1 tsp. tomato paste

-½ tsp. potato flour (optional)

Day 12

Don't listen to people who tell you that sweet equals unhealthy. Today's Cocoa & Coffee Smoothie is a drink to provide you with the right dose of magnesium and give you the necessary power to not only survive but also rock the day on the highest speed possible. The only savoury meal in today's plan is the Broccoli & Egg Salad, also known as a protein & vitamin bomb. It's always good to keep your tummy filled with veggies and some healthy fats, so you'll definitely find this lunch amazing. Speaking of healthy desserts again, let's shed some light on those Oat Carrot Cookies that actually constitute a full meal. Surprised? Wait until you try them!

Oat Carrot Cookies

Cocoa & Coffee Smothie

 2   309   5'

1. Add the espresso, cooked millet and other ingredients to the blender and mix until perfectly smooth.
2. Pour the smoothie into glasses and serve immediately.

-250ml espresso, cooled (8.5 fl oz)

-120g millet, cooked and cooled

-250 ml almond milk (8.5 fl oz)

-1 tbsp. peanut butter

-2 tsp. brown sugar

Broccoli & Egg Salad

 4   260   10'

1. In a medium pot, bring water to a boil. Divide the broccoli into several smaller chunks and cook it for 5 to 7 minutes over low heat. Rinse the broccoli with water.
2. In the meantime, add eggs to a separate pot filled with boiling water. Cook them for 7 minutes. Allow the eggs to cool, peel them and cut in four parts.
3. Drain the corn kernels and add them to a large bowl with the romaine lettuce. Season with salt and pepper. Stir until well combined.
4. Mix all ingredients of the Caesar sauce in a food processor.
5. Add the broccoli, eggs, and season the salad with salt and pepper.
6. Top with the Caesar sauce and grated parmesan.

-250g broccoli (8.8 oz)

-4 eggs

-100g corn kernels (3.5 oz)

-175g (6.2 oz) romaine lettuce, chopped

-4 tbsp. grated parmesan

-Salt and pepper to taste

Caesar sauce: (6 tbsp. mayonnaise +
2 tsp. French mustard + 3 tsp. honey +
2 tsp. light soy sauce + 1 garlic clove +
salt and pepper to taste)

Oat Carrot Cookies

 3   240   12'

1. Preheat the oven to 170 degrees.
2. In a large bowl, combine the oat flakes with flour, baking soda, and cinnamon.
3. In a separate bowl, combine the egg with melted coconut oil, vanilla extract, and honey. Add the dry ingredients and mix until well combined.
4. Stir in the grated carrot.
5. Spoon the batter and form flat discs. Place the cookies on a baking sheet and lightly flatten them with your hand.
6. Bake for 12 minutes.

-1 medium carrot, peeled and finely grated

-100g instant oat flakes (3.5 oz)

-100g rye flour (3.5 oz)

-1 tsp. baking soda

-1 tsp. ground cinnamon

-3 tbsp. coconut oil

-1 large egg

-1 tsp. vanilla extract

-100ml honey (3.4 fl oz)

Day 13

Since its best to consume fruits early in the day, adding them to your breakfast seems like the most reasonable choice. That being said, the Mango & Maracuya Oatmeal will provide your system with its daily portion of simple carbohydrates. As the day moves on, you'll cut down on carbohydrates with the Artichoke & Dried Tomatoes pasta – a healthy and juicy meal for a lunch. The dinner, in turn, will consist of the Chicken & Egg Fried rice so that you may indulge in Asian flavours while keeping your calories intake well-balanced.

Mango & Maracuya Oatmeal

Mango & Maracuya Oatmeal

 2   215   7'

1. Add the oat flakes to a pot. Cover with water and bring to a boil. Reduce heat to low and cook for 5 minutes, stirring from time to time. Remove from the heat.
2. Add milk. Pour the oatmeal into bowls. Sprinkle with sugar and drizzle with orange juice.
3. Top with chopped mango and maracuya. Serve immediately.

-30g instant oat flakes (1.0 oz)
-250ml water (8.5 fl oz)
-80ml milk (2.7 fl oz)

-1 tbsp. brown sugar
-2 tbsp. fresh orange juice

-½ mango
-1 maracuya

Artichoke & Dried Tomatoes Pasta

 2   280   10'

1. Cook the pasta al dente in salted water (4-5 minutes)
2. Heat the olive oil in a non-stick frying pan. Add the sliced garlic cloves and saute until golden, stirring constantly. Add the chopped ham and dried oregano, and saute for 30 more seconds.
3. Add the chopped artichoke hearts, dried tomatoes, sunflower oil, parsley, and cook for 30 seconds.
4. Add the drained pasta and season it with freshly ground pepper. Toss well and cook for 30 more seconds.
5. Garnish with freshly grated parmesan and serve immediately.

-100g whole-grain penne pasta (3.5 oz)
-1 tbsp. extra virgin olive oil
-3 garlic cloves
-2 slices of prosciutto ham

-1 tsp. dried oregano
-¼ artichoke hearts
-4 chunks of dried tomatoes

-1 tbsp. sunflower oil
-1 tsp. fresh parsley, chopped
-Grated parmesan for garnish

Chicken & Egg Fried Rice

 2   410   10'

1. Cook the rice ahead of time. Drain and allow it to cool.
2. Drizzle the chopped chicken breast with lime juice, season with salt and pepper, and combine with 1 tablespoon of coconut oil.
3. Add eggs to a small bowl and season them with salt and pepper. Beat the eggs with sesame oil.
4. In a large non-stick pan, heat 2 tablespoons of coconut oil and add the onion. Saute for 1 minute.
5. Add the garlic and saute for another minute. After that, add the carrot and leek, and saute for 2 minutes, stirring constantly.
6. With a spatula, set the vegetables on the side of the pan and add the chicken with the chilli pepper. Cook for 2 minutes and combine with your veggies.
7. Add rice and cook for 2 minutes, stirring from time to time. Stir in the fish sauce and let it evaporate (not longer than 3 minutes).
8. Pour in the egg mixture and fry it for about 1 minute until it stiffens. Toss with chives and cilantro. Drizzle with lime juice.

-100g jasmine rice (3.5 oz)
-250g boneless, skinless chicken breast, diced (8.8 oz)
-½ carrot, finely grated
-½ onion, finely chopped

-¼ leek (white part), thinly sliced
-3 garlic cloves, finely grated
-1 chili pepper, finely chopped
-3 tbsp. chopped chives
-2 eggs

-2 tsp. sesame oil
-3 tbsp. coconut oil
-2 tbsp. fish sauce (optional)
-Fresh cilantro leaves for garnish
-Juice from 1 lime

Day 14

Day 14 is going to be rich in proteins, mostly from eggs and chicken meat. Shakshuka will be your first meal; this Tunisian breakfast consists of eggs cooked in tomatoes, with basil and garlic to add more flavour and fragrance to the dish. The Chicken & Broccoli Fried Rice will provide you with a generous portion of both proteins, vitamins, and complex carbohydrates in the form of a quick Chinese style stir-fry. Asia will also rule the roost for the dinner. This time, we'll combine some oriental yet classic flavours with the Sweet & Sour Chicken. It will surely make your palate go crazy – in a positive and healthy way, of course.

Shakshuka

Shakshuka

  2   230   5'

1. Melt the butter in a medium non-stick pan.
2. Add the sliced garlic and saute it for 30 seconds.
3. Add the tomatoes. Season with salt, pepper, oregano, and chili. Cook for about 4 minutes on medium heat.
4. Beat in the eggs and season them with salt. Cover the pan with a lid and cook for about 3 minutes until the egg white stiffens.

-2 tomatoes, blanched, peeled and cut in quarters

-2 tbsp. unsalted butter

-½ small garlic clove

A pinch of each: salt, freshly ground pepper, dried oregano, chili powder

-2 large eggs

-Fresh basil leaves for garnish

Chicken & Broccoli Fried Rice

  2   550 15'

1. Cook the rice for about 10-13 minutes over low heat and drain it afterwards.
2. When you're halfway done with cooking the rice, heat the coconut oil in a large pan or wok.
3. Add the chicken and sauté it for 2-3 minutes until cooked through.
4. Add the broccoli with carrot. Fry the vegetables for 5 minutes, stirring constantly. Should the veggies stick to the pan, add a splash of water and shake the pan two or three times.
5. Add the grated ginger and garlic and cook them for 30 seconds.
6. Add the peanut butter and soy sauce, and combine them with your vegetables.
7. Stir in the rice and cook for 1 minute.
8. Drizzle with sesame oil and sprinkle with nigella seeds.

-100g rice (3.5 oz)

-250g boneless, skinless chicken breast, diced (8.8 oz)

-250g broccoli, divided into florets (8.8 oz)

-1 carrot, cut in stripes

-2 tbsp. coconut oil

-1 tbsp. grated ginger

-2 garlic cloves

-2 tbsp. light soy sauce

-1 tbsp. peanut butter

-2 tsp. sesame oil

-1 tbsp. nigella seeds

Sweet & Sour Chicken

  2   470   10'

1. Combine the vinegar with sugar and 3 tablespoons of water. Set aside.
2. Heat the coconut in a wok. Add the chicken and fry it on each side for about 5 minutes, adding the ginger, garlic, and white pepper at the end.
3. Add the pepper and carrot, and cook for about 3 minutes. After that, add the pineapple, stir well, and continue cooking for 2 minutes.
4. Increase the heat and pour in the vinegar mixture. Stir well and bring to a boil. Cook for about 2 minutes.
5. Stir in the ketchup/tomato puree and cook for 1 minute.

-350g boneless, skinless chicken breast, diced (12.3 oz)

-1 red bell pepper, diced

-1 carrot, cut in stripes

-¼ pineapple, peeled and thinly sliced

-1 tbsp. potato flour

-2 tsp. freshly grated ginger

-1 garlic clove

-60ml rice vinegar (2.0 fl oz)

-4 tbsp. brown unrefined sugar

-A pinch of white pepper

-1 tbsp. coconut oil

-3 tbsp. ketchup or tomato puree

Day 15

Have you ever tried using quinoa instead of rice of millet for a salad? If not, it's high time you did it. Quinoa is a fancy and healthy way of incorporating complex carbs that are not only nutritious but also very tasty. If you're in a hurry today, you're going to find this Pasta Salad served in a jar extremely handy – just a couple of moves and you can indulge in a juicy meal with lots of complex carbs, vitamins, full proteins, and unsaturated fats. Craving for some crispy chicken strips without ingesting massive amounts of cholesterol? Well, here's something for you – the Almond-coated Chicken Strips. Bring your pots, clean the prep station, and get ready for some easy cooking!

Almond-coated Chicken Strips

Quinoa & Fried Cheese Salad

 2   625   7'

1. Rinse the quinoa with water. In a medium pot, bring water to a boil and add the quinoa. Cover with a lid and cook the quinoa for 2-3 minutes. Turn off the heat and leave the pot for 5 minutes until the quinoa absorbs all liquid.
2. Combine the quinoa with toasted almond flakes and the diced radish.
3. Heat a large non-stick pan over medium heat. Add the halloumi cheese and fry for about 2 minutes per side.
4. Top the salad with the fried halloumi cheese.
5. In a small bowl, combine all ingredients of the vinaigrette.
6. Top the salad with the sauce.

-170g quinoa (6.0 oz)

-30g almond flakes, lightly toasted (1.0 oz)

-25g fresh spinach leaves (0.9 oz)

-200g halloumi cheese, roughly sliced (7.0 oz)

-55g radish, diced (1.9 oz)

Vinaigrette: (4 tbsp. olive oil + 3 tbsp. lemon juice + 2 tsp. maple syrup + salt and pepper to taste)

Pasta Salad In a Jar

 2   511   10'

1. Prepare the sauce: in a small bowl, whisk the lemon juice with salt. Add the garlic and gradually pour in the olive oil, whisking constantly. Season with pepper, oregano, and additional salt (if you consider it necessary), and stir until combined. Pour in the sauce so that it stays at the bottom of a jar.
2. Cook the pasta until al dente (4-5 minutes). Add the pasta to the jar.
3. Add the drained tuna, rocket lettuce, baby mozzarella, and cherry tomatoes.
4. Sprinkle with the chilli pepper and add olives.
5. Seal the jar.
6. Shake the jar before serving the salad.

-75g uncooked whole-grain pasta (2.6 oz)

-100g canned tuna (3.5 oz)

-A handful of rocket lettuce

-125g cherry tomatoes, sliced in halves (4.4 oz)

-125g baby mozzarella (4.4 oz)

-½ red chilli pepper, finely chopped

-130g black olives, sliced (4.6 oz)

For the sauce: (1 tbsp. lemon juice + 1/3 tsp. salt + 2 grated garlic cloves + 3 tbsp. extra virgin olive oil + pepper and dried oregano to taste)

Almond-coated Chicken Strips

 4   347   10'

1. Cook the broccoli florets in salted water for about 5-7 minutes. Drain and set aside.
2. Prepare the sauce: combine the yoghurt with the garlic, salt, pepper, and chopped herbs.
3. Cut the chicken breast into thin fillets, then cut each fillet in 3 stripes. Season with salt and pepper.
4. Dip the chicken in milk and then in the lightly beaten egg. Coat with almond flakes mixed with ground breadcrumbs.
5. Fry the chicken strips for 3-4 minutes per side until golden-brown.
6. Serve the chicken with the broccoli and herbal sauce.

-600g (21.2 oz) boneless, skinless chicken breast

-Salt and pepper to taste

-125ml milk (4.2 fl oz)

-1 egg

-100g almond flakes (3.5 oz)

-50g ground breadcrumbs (1.8 oz)

-1 broccoli, divided into florets

For the herbal sauce: (2 tbsp. mayonnaise + 180g (6.3 oz) yoghurt + ½ finely grated garlic clove + 4 tbsp. each: chopped basil leaves, parsley, dill, mint + salt and pepper to taste)

Day 16

Most people, when thinking of the sea-food diet, say that they see food and they eat it. While their excuse seems legit, our sea-food will be incorporated into the plan in a lean way, in the form of Shrimp & Pomelo Salad. During the lunch, you'll have the opportunity to convince yourself to trying raw meat in the form of the Beef Tartare. For dinner, you're going to upgrade your shakshuka with a red bell pepper and a cottage sausage. Remember, it's all about combining whole foods with deep flavours.

Beef Tartare

Shrimp & Pomelo Salad

 2   315   15'

1. In a small bowl, combine all ingredients of the dressing.
2. In a medium non-stick pan, heat the coconut oil. Add shrimps and cook for about 2 minutes. Remove from the heat.
3. Place the cooked shrimps to the salad bowl. Add the pomelo chunks, grated carrot, and mung bean sprouts.
4. Top with the dressing and stir well. Serve in small plates.

-300g black tiger shrimps, peeled and deveined (10.6 oz)
-4 tsp. freshly grated ginger
-1 tsp. fish sauce

-1 pomelo, peeled and cut into chunks
-20g carrot, finely grated (0.7 oz)
-2 tsp. coconut oil
-50g. mung bean sprouts (1.8 oz)

For the lime-sesame dressing:
(4 tbsp. lime juice + 4 tsp. honey +
4 tsp. rice vinegar + 4 tbsp. sesame oil +
a pinch of chili flakes)

Beef Tartare

 2   408   5'

1. Add the soy sauce to the finely chopped beef. Combine the seasoned meat with egg yolks, pepper, and truffle oil. Season with sea salt.
2. Spread the beef tartare over the bread and top with the onion, spinach, and dried tomatoes. Season with salt and pepper. Drizzle the tartare with more truffle oil.

-200g beef sirloin, finely chopped (7.0 oz)
-1 tbsp. light soy sauce
-2 egg yolks

-1 tbsp. truffle oil
-Freshly ground black pepper to taste
-4 slices of whole-wheat bread

-Several leaves of spinach
-Several slices of sweet onion

Shakshuka with Sausage & Red Bell Pepper   2   205   10'

1. In a non-stick pan, heat the olive oil. Add the garlic and sauté for 30 seconds. Add the red bell pepper and sausage, and sauté again for 1 minute.
2. Add the tomatoes. Season with salt, pepper, cumin, and oregano, and stir well. Cook on high heat for about 4 minutes.
3. Beat in the eggs and season them with salt. Reduce the heat, cover the pan with a lid and cook the eggs for about 3 minutes until the egg whites stiffen.

-2 tomatoes, blanched, peeled, and cut in quarters
-½ tbsp.. extra virgin olive oil
-½ small garlic clove, thinly sliced

-100g (3.5 oz) red bell pepper, finely chopped
-60g (2.1 oz) cottage sausage, sliced
-2 eggs

-A pinch of each: dried oregano and cumin
-Salt and freshly ground black pepper to taste
-Fresh basil leaves for garnish

Day 17

Imagine waking up after a long night and having a myriad of tasks to accomplish. How would you feel? Frustrated? Well, the Green Tea Smoothie will wash away all frustration and, instead, will pump lots of energy into your body. Fancy the idea of such a breakfast? You'd better get ready for a juicy lunch which consists of the Salmon & Basmati Rice Salad. We all know that fish are rich in omega fat acids and, at the same time, come with plenty of proteins to take care of your muscles after, say, a hard workout. Speaking of proteins, are you ready for a clash of the two opposite worlds? If the answer is yes, you'll without a doubt love the Fried Eggs With Avocado & Hummus for dinner.

Fried Eggs With Hummus & Avocado

Green Tea Smoothie

 2　 220　🕐 5'

1. Brew the tea and allow it to cool.
2. Peel the melon, deseed it, and take out the flesh.
3. Put the melon in a blender and add the peeled kiwi, apple juice, lime juice, rinsed spinach leaves, and tea.
4. Process for 1 minute on high speed.

-500ml green tea (16.9 fl oz)
-600g melon (21.2 oz)

-2 ripe kiwis
-250ml apple juice (8.5 oz)

-Juice from 1 lime
-2 handfuls of fresh spinach leaves

Salmon & Basmati Rice Salad

 2　 250　 20'

1. Cook rice in salted water over medium heat for 13 minutes.
2. In the meantime, cook the salmon in a non-stick pan, about 5 minutes per side.
3. Roughly chop the salmon and combine it with the rice, parsley, chives, and lime juice. Season with salt and pepper.
4. Combine the salad with cream just before serving.

-100g basmati rice (3.5 oz)
-250g raw skinless salmon (8.8 oz)
-10g chopped parsley (0.3 oz)

-10g chopped chives (0.3 oz)
-Juice from 2 limes

-Zest from 2 lime
-100ml (3.4 fl oz) cream, 22% of fat

Fried Eggs With Hummus & Avocado

 2　 490　 5'

1. Place the hummus on plates and sprinkle it with cumin. Add the sliced avocado, rocket lettuce, and tomatoes. Season with salt and pepper, and drizzle with olive oil.
2. In a medium non-stick pan, toast the sesame seeds and sprinkle them over the salad's ingredients.
3. Heat the sesame oil and fry the eggs for about 3 minutes until the whites are stiffened.

-6 tbsp. hummus
-2 pinches of cumin
-1 avocado, peeled and deseeded
-A handful of cherry tomatoes, cut in quarters

-Several rocket lettuce leaves
-2 tbsp. sesame seeds
-2 eggs

-1 tbsp. sesame oil
-1 tbsp. olive oil
-2 slices of whole-wheat bread

Day 18

Today's meal plan will be all about vegetarian recipes (vegetarian, not vegan – know the difference!) Moreover, the couscous will be the hero of our two meals. It'll make its appearance for the first time during breakfast, as you'll revel in Lemon, Zucchini & Feta Couscous full of Greek flavours and fried veggies. Next, there will be the Grilled Eggplant & Couscous Salad that will take your green experience to a next level – the level from which you won't be willing to step down. Finally, the couscous isn't the only ingredient that will be repeated today, as zucchini will also bless you with its undisputed nutritional values for dinner in the form of the Boiled Eggs with Zucchini & Tomatoes.

Lemon & Zucchini Couscous

Lemon & Zucchini Couscous

 2 475 12'

1. In a large non-stick pan, heat the olive oil and add the garlic. Sauté for 1 minute. Add the zucchini and cook for about 5 minutes, stirring from time to time until softened. Season with lemon zest, salt, pepper, and sauté for another minute.
2. In a large pot, bring the broth to a boil with the lemon juice. Remove from the heat, add couscous, and cover the pot with a lid.
3. Remove the lead, stir the couscous with a fork, and add the zucchini. Season with salt and pepper to taste.
4. Garnish with mint and the crumbled feta cheese.

-½ tsp. lemon zest

-150ml vegetable broth (5.1 fl oz)

-1 tsp. lemon juice

-150g couscous (5.3 oz)

-A handful of mint leaves

Grilled Eggplant & Couscous Salad

 2 350 15'

1. Season the eggplant generously with salt and set aside for 15 minutes.
2. In the meantime, pour the hot broth over the couscous. Cover with a lid and set aside for 10 minutes.
3. Heat a non-stick grill pan and add the eggplant. Season with salt, drizzle with olive oil and grill for 5 minutes per side. Remove from the heat.
4. Roughly chop the cooked eggplant and drizzle it with the lemon juice. Combine the couscous with olive oil and mint. Add the eggplant, feta cheese, and cherry tomatoes.
5. Drizzle with olive oil and season with salt and pepper.

-½ large eggplant, cut in 1-cm slices

-90g couscous (3.2 oz)

-125ml vegetable broth (4.2 oz)

-Juice from ¼ lemon

-1 tbsp. chopped mint leaves

-60g feta cheese (2.1 oz)

-100g cherry tomatoes, cut in halves (3.5 oz)

-1 tbsp. olive oil

Boiled Eggs with Zucchini & Tomatoes

 2 175 10'

1. Heat the olive oil in a medium non-stick pan. Add the onion and sauté for 1 minute on medium heat. Add the garlic and chili, and sauté for another minute.
2. Add the zucchini, pepper, and pour in the olive oil. Cook for 2-3 minutes, stirring from time to time. Season with salt so that the vegetables get softened over time.
3. Stir in the tomatoes and season them with salt and pepper. Cook for about 4 minutes, stirring from time to time.
4. Beat in the eggs and cover the pan with a lid. Cook for 3 minutes until the egg white is stiffened and the yolk is still runny.
5. Serve with fresh basil leaves.

-2 tsp. olive oil

-½ small onion, finely chopped

-½ garlic clove, finely chopped

-½ chili pepper, finely chopped

-150g zucchini, diced (5.3 oz)

-½ red bell pepper, diced

-3 medium tomatoes, blanched, peeled, and diced

-2 eggs

-¼ tsp. ground turmeric

-¼ tsp. ground cumin

-Salt and pepper to taste

Day 19

We're more than halfway through our journey with the 30-day whole foods plan. I bet you're excited to see what's on today's menu. We're going to greet the morning with the Double-layer Strawberry smoothie. This drink is like a heaven to one's taste buds, but you'd better see it to yourself – or should I say 'taste' instead of 'see'? Anyway, the second course calls for the Egg & Black Olive Paste Sandwich. This lunch will keep you full of energy with the combination of saturated and unsaturated fats, both of which are essential for your body's well-being. If you're looking for some diversity in your noodles menu, here's some good news – your dinner consists of the Grilled Zucchini & Chilli Rice Noodles.

Double-layer Strawberry Smoothie

Double-layer Strawberry Smoothie 2 230 5'

1. Mix all ingredients of the red layer in a food processor and pour it into glasses.
2. Mix all ingredients of the white layer in a food processor ant pour it on the top of the red layer.

For the red layer:
-400g strawberries (14.1 oz)
-2 tbsp. maple syrup
-2 tbsp. lemon juice

For the white layer:
-2 bananas, peeled and sliced
-4 tbsp. natural yoghurt

-200g pineapple flesh (7.0 oz)
-2 tbsp. lemon juice

Egg & Black Olives Paste Sandwich 4 315 10'

1. Hard boil the eggs in water for 8-10 minutes.
2. In the meantime, place the olives in a blender. Add the olive oil, garlic, walnuts, parmesan, and anchovies, and blend everything together to the consistency of a paste. If needed, add a splash of water and blend again for a while.
3. Season with thyme, salt, and pepper.
4. Spread the paste over the bread and top it with sliced eggs. Drizzle with olive oil and sprinkle with fresh thyme.
5. Season with salt and freshly ground pepper to taste.

-150g black olives (5.3 oz)
-2 tbsp. extra virgin olive oil
-½ garlic clove
-30g walnuts (1.0 oz)

-1 tsp. grated parmesan
-1 anchovies fillet
-½ tsp. fresh thyme

-4 slices of whole-wheat bread
-4 eggs
-Sea salt and pepper to taste

Grilled Zucchini & Chili Rice Noodles 2 600 15'

1. Season the zucchini with salt and cook it in the grill pan for 15 minutes, stirring from time to time. At the end, add the chopped peanuts and lightly toast them.
2. In the meantime, combine all ingredients of the sauce in a small bowl. Add the sliced chili and chopped chives.
3. Cook the noodles according to the package directions. Usually, you'll just have to pour the hot water over the noodles and wait 5 minutes.
4. Drain the noodles and cut them into 10-cm pieces.
5. Return the noodles to the pot, add the sauce and stir well.
6. Add the zucchini and peanuts, followed by the chives. Stir in half of the mint and cilantro.
7. Place the noodles in plates and garnish with the remaining mint and cilantro.

-200g rice noodles (7.0 oz)
-1 zucchini, diced
-4 tbsp. peanuts
-1-2 large chili peppers, sliced

-2 stalks of chives, chopped
-A handful of each: fresh mint and
 cilantro leaves

For the sauce: (1 garlic clove, finely grated
+ 2 tbsp. fish sauce + juice from 1 lime
+ 1 tbsp. rice vinegar + 1 tbsp. brown sugar)

Day 20

Nothing tastes better in the morning than a bowl of juicy pasta. If it's Pasta Caprese, it's all the better. Fresh tagliatelle, tomatoes, extra virgin olive oil, and mozzarella – literally everything you need you need to start the day with a culinary experience worth these 10 minutes of preparation. The moment you open your lunch box, you'll have the opportunity to please yourself with Shrimp Toasts, ingesting lean proteins in the company of complex carbohydrates and some chili mayo to make the twist in these sandwiches. As we move towards the dinner, it's time to taste a Mexican specialty, i.e. Guacamole With Radish. Making your life easier has never been so tasty!

Shrimp Toasts

Pasta Caprese

 2   650   10'

1. In a bowl, combine the tomatoes with salt, pepper, vinegar, and olive oil.
2. Take the 1/3 of tomatoes of the bowl and mix them with an immersion blender. Add the mixed tomatoes to the bowl again.
3. In the meantime, cook the pasta al dente, about 4 to 5 minutes. Drain the pasta and return it to the pot. Add the butter and stir well to combine.
4. Add the tomatoes, chili flakes, basil and stir to combine.
5. Place the salad in the bowls and add the mozzarella. Garnish with fresh basil.

-2 tomatoes, blanched, peeled, and diced (water saved)

-2 tsp. rice vinegar

-4 tbsp. extra virgin olive oil

-140g whole-grain tagliatelle pasta (4.9 oz)

-1 tbsp. unsalted butter

-125g mozzarella, torn (4.4 oz)

-1 tsp. chili flakes

-2 handfuls of basil leaves, chopped

-Salt and pepper to taste

Shrimp Toasts

 4   325   10'

1. In a small bowl, combine all ingredients of the sauce. Place the sauce in the fridge as you prepare the toasts.
2. Heat 1 tbsp. of olive oil in a non-stick pan. Add the shrimps and cook them for 2 minutes per side. Chop the shrimps and set aside.
3. Toast the bread in a grill pan and spread the sauce over each slice.
4. Top 4 slices with the lettuce, red bell pepper stripes, and chopped shrimps.
5. Season with salt and pepper, and close your sandwiches with the remaining slices.

-8 slices of whole-grain bread

-15 black tiger shrimps, peeled and deveined

-2 red bell peppers, deseeded and cut in stripes, lengthwise

-Several leaves of lettuce

For the sauce: (2 tbsp. sweet chili sauce

+ 3 tbsp. chopped parsley

+ 4 tbsp. mayonnaise)

Guacamole With Radish

 2   550   5'

1. Drizzle the avocado with the lime juice and add the tomato.
2. Add the radish, onion, garlic, cilantro, and olive oil. Season with salt and stir well to combine.
3. Season with cumin and tabasco sauce.
4. Serve with the toasted tortilla.

-1 ripe avocado, peeled, deseeded, and diced

-2 tsp. lime juice

-½ tomato, blanched, peeled, and diced

-4-5 radishes, roughly chopped

-1 tbsp. onion, finely chopped

-1 small garlic clove, grated

-2 handfuls of fresh cilantro leaves

-A pinch of cumin

-3-4 drops of tabasco sauce

-1 whole-grain toasted tortilla for serving

Day 21

If you're looking to have your favourite scrambled eggs in a more nutritious and less fatty way, these Scrambled Eggs With Avocado will do the job. Avocado is known for its healthy fats and, when combined with chives, the creamy texture of the fruit gains the so-called punch when added to eggs. The lunch calls for Asparagus & Bacon Sandwiches. The bacon, although kept in moderation, will add the wonderful crispiness to the sandwiches, especially when juxtaposed with asparagus and pine nuts. It's a truly soul-pleasing and nutritious way to enjoy your afternoon lunch break. For dinner, you're going to enjoy an unusual yet brilliant combination of cheese and fruits in the form of the Grape & Goat Cheese Salad.

Asparagus & Bacon Sandwiches

Scrambled Eggs With Avocado

 2   330   10'

1. Sprinkle the avocado with chives. Season with salt and pepper.
2. In a medium non-stick pan, heat the butter and beat in the eggs. Stir the eggs from time to time until both the whites and yolks are stiffened.
3. Remove from the heat and gently stir in the avocado.
4. Serve the scrambled eggs with bread.

-1 ripe avocado, peeled, deseeded, and diced

-2 tbsp. chopped chives
-1 tbsp. butter

-2 eggs
-2 slices of whole-grain bread

Asparagus & Bacon Sandwiches

 2   320   15'

1. Wash the asparagus and break off the hard parts, and peel them. Cook the asparagus in a grill pan for 5 minutes, flipping them each minute.
2. Toast the pine nuts in a non-stick pan for 2 minutes on medium-low heat.
3. In the meantime, heat a non-stick pan and add the bacon. Cook until crispy, 4-5 minutes on medium heat.
4. Slice the ciabatta bun in halves. Top each half with the rocket lettuce, crumbled parmesan cheese, and drizzle with olive oil. Add the roughly chopped asparagus and bacon.
5. Sprinkle with the pine nuts and season with salt and pepper. Drizzle with olive oil and top with the yoghurt-mayonnaise sauce.

-6 green asparagus
-2 tbsp. pine nuts
-4 slices of bacon
-1 ciabatta bun

-A handful of rocket lettuce
-2 tbsp. extra virgin olive oil
-Crumbled parmesan cheese for garnish

For the sauce: (2 tbsp. mayonnaise + 3 tbsp. natural yoghurt + 3 tbsp. lemon juice)

Grapes & Goat Cheese Salad

 2   425   5'

1. Rinse the rocket lettuce and season it with salt, pepper, olive oil, and lemon juice. Place the lettuce in large plates.
2. Add the grapes, crumbled cheese, sunflower seed kernels, and stir gently.
3. Mix all ingredients of the sauce in a small bowl.
4. Top the salad with sauce. Serve with bread.

-60g rocket lettuce (2.1 oz)
-10 white grapes, cut in halves
-40g goat cheese (1.4 oz)
-2 tbsp. sunflower seed kernels

-4 slices of whole-grain rye bread
-1 tbsp. olive oil
-2 tsp. lemon juice
-Salt and pepper to taste

For the sauce: (4 tbsp. balsamic vinegar + 2 tbsp. extra virgin olive oil + 2 tbsp. honey + a pinch of each: cinnamon, salt, freshly ground black pepper)

Day 22

The Maple Syrup Yoghurt for breakfast is a very smart way of getting your daily portion of simple sugars in an almost instant way. Practical values aside, the yoghurt is topped with fresh fruits, including strawberries, blueberries, and banana, so you can already imagine the fruit punch explosion in such a meal. After receiving such a tasty and energizing vitamin shot, it's time to slow down a bit, so you'll appreciate hands down the most delicious toasts that combine both sweet and savory flavours – Goat Cheese & Thyme Toasts. The Dinner is going to surprise you with its form, as it's not a usual thing to consume Chia Seeds in Coconut Milk as a main course. Nonetheless, It's without a doubt a healthy and satisfying meal.

Syrup Yoghurt

Maple Syrup Yoghurt

 2   315   5'

1. Pour the yoghurt into the bowls.
2. Add the maple syrup and top with the fruits.

-360g natural yoghurt (12.7 oz)

-6 tbsp. maple syrup

-140g banana, sliced (4.9 oz)

-50g raspberries (1.8 oz)

-50g strawberries, cut in quarters (1.8 oz)

Goat Cheese & Thyme Toasts

 2   407   5'

1. Preheat the oven to 175 degrees.
2. Broil the bread in the oven for 5 minutes.
3. Drizzle the bread slices with olive oil and top them with the goat cheese and grapes.
4. Season with pepper and thyme.

-6 slices of whole-grain rye bread

-2 tbsp. olive oil

-70g goat cheese (2.5 oz)

-12 black grapes, cut in halves

-Several leaves of fresh thyme

-Freshly ground black pepper to taste

Chia Seeds in Coconut Milk

 2   422   10'

1. For the chia seeds in coconut milk: Add the chia seeds to a medium saucepan. Pour in the milk and water. Add the xylitol and vanilla bean paste, and cook under a lid on low heat for 10 minutes.
2. For the caramelized bananas: Heat a non-stick pan and add the sugar. Shake the pan several times to spread the sugar all over the surface. Wait for the sugar to dissolve and add the banana. Cook the banana for about 2 minutes per side until golden-brown. Drizzle the banana with lemon juice.
3. Top the chia and coconut mixture with caramelized bananas and serve immediately.

-40g chia seeds (1.4 oz)

-200ml coconut milk (6.8 fl oz)

-150ml water (5.1 fl oz)

-1 tsp. vanilla bean paste

-1 banana, cut in halves and then in quarters lengthwise

-2tsb. Xylitol

-2 tbsp. lemon juice

Day 23

As soon as you fall in love with smoothies, you'll start craving for more and more variations of those power-drinks. That being said, the Kale & Kiwi Smoothie is going to rock your world. Its green power will surely keep you full of vitamins and increase your serotonin levels for the rest of the day. Another position in today's vegetarian menu is the Tofu & Ginger Stir-fry. Revel in fried noodles packed with veggies and topped with tofu – they are worth every single bite. Last but not least, the dinner will consist of Egg Muffins, a pretty, hearty and fun meal that tastes even better than the restaurant version.

Tofu & Ginger Stir Fry

Kale & Kiwi Smoothie

 2   270   5'

1. Place the kale leaves in a blender.
2. Add the banana, kiwi, apple juice, coconut milk, and lime juice.
3. Mix thoroughly for 2 minutes. Serve immediately.

-60g kale leaves (2.1 oz)

-1 banana

-1 kiwi

-125ml apple juice (4.2 fl oz)

-125ml coconut milk (4.2 fl oz)

-1 tbsp. lime juice

Tofu & Ginger Stir Fry

 2   485   10'

1. Cook the rice noodles for about 5 minutes and drain them afterwards.
2. In the meantime, heat the coconut oil in a wok. Addthe ginger, garlic, and carrot. Cook for 5 minutes on medium heat, stirring from time to time.
3. Add tofu and cook for about 2-3 minutes.
4. Stir in the noodles and cook for 1-2 minutes, stirring constantly.
5. Pour in the soy sauce. Add the chili pepper and cook for 1 minute.
6. Turn off the heat. Drizzle the stir-fry with olive oil, lime juice, and garnish with chives. Stir well to combine.

-100g rice noodles (3.5 oz)

-1 tbsp. coconut oil

-1 garlic clove, finely grated

-3 tsp. freshly grated ginger

-1 carrot, roughly grated

-100g tofu, diced (3.5 oz)

-5 tbsp. light soy sauce

-1 tsp. chili pepper, finely chopped

-2 tbsp. sesame oil

-3 tbsp. chopped chives

-Juice from 1 lime

Egg Muffins

 2   163   15'

1. Preheat the oven to 180 degrees.
2. Beat the eggs with garlic, salt, pepper, and chives. Add the spinach, zucchini, goat cheese, and pepper. Stir with a fork.
3. Butter a muffin tin. Fill the tin with the egg batter and bake for 15 minutes.

-50g chopped spinach leaves (1.8 oz)

-¼ zucchini, grated

-50g shredded goat cheese (1.8 oz)

-¼ red bell pepper, diced

-2 large eggs

-½ garlic clove, grated

-1 tsp. chopped chives

-Salt and pepper to taste

Day 24

People believe not to trust those who don't like pancakes. If you share this opinion, you'll be delighted by the fact that today's breakfast consists of fluffy Ricotta Pancakes. Topped with some cream cheese and maple syrup, these pancakes are yet another reason to switch to whole foods. Anyway, today's lunch calls for an exotic meal, which is the Lentil & Meat Pilaf. This hearty one-pan dish is not only quick and easy to prepare but also gluten-free, so if you're one of those folks suffering from gluten allergy, you may consider yourself lucky. Finally, as the sunset draws near, you have a full bowl of the Orange Chicken Salad. We all know how well poultry and fruits work together, so it goes without saying that this nutritious and juicy gourmet dinner will make you remember this combination for the rest of your healthy life!

Lentil & Meat Pilaf

Ricotta Pancakes

 3   502   12'

1. In a large bowl, combine the flour with baking soda and salt. Set aside.
2. In a separate bowl, combine the ricotta cheese with eggs, coconut oil, milk, and honey.
3. Combine the dry and wet ingredients so that they form a smooth batter.
4. Heat a large non-stick pan and add 1 heaping tablespoon of the pancake batter, cooking 4 pancakes at a time. Cook each pancake for 2 minutes. Top the pancakes with banana slices (2 slices for each pancake), flip them and cook for another 2 minutes.
5. Serve with cream cheese and maple syrup.

-160g buckwheat flour (5.6 oz)

-3 tbsp. honey

-2 tsp. baking soda

-A pinch of salt

-250g ricotta cheese (8.8 oz)

-2 eggs

-2 tbsp. coconut oil

-60ml milk (2.0 fl oz)

-2 bananas, sliced

Lentil & Meat Pilaf

 2   465   15'

1. Heat 1 tablespoon of olive oil in a large non-stick pan. Add the onion and sauté for 2 minutes until softened.
2. Add the veal and sauté until cooked through. Season with sweet and hot paprika, oregano, and cumin.
3. Stir in the lentil and rice. Cook for 2 minutes, add the zucchini and cook for another 2 minutes. Season with salt and pepper.
4. Pour in the broth. Bring to a boil and cook under a lid for 15 minutes until the rice and lentil are soft.
5. In a food processor, mix the parsley with olive oil, garlic and salt until smooth.
6. Serve the pilaf in large place and top with the parsley mixture.

-1 sweet onion, finely chopped

-150g ground veal (5.3 oz)

-4 tbsp. green lentil

-50g white rice (1.8 oz)

-125g zucchini, diced (4.4 oz)

-250ml vegetable broth (8.5 fl oz)

-½ tsp. dried oregano

-½ tsp. cumin

-½ tsp. sweet paprika

-½ tsp hot paprika

-3 tbsp. chopped parsley

-½ small garlic clove

Orange Chicken

 2   509   12'

1. In a small bowl or cup, combine all ingredients of the sauce. Season with salt and pepper and set aside.
2. Season the chicken breast with salt and rub it with olive oil.
3. Heat the olive oil in a large non-stick pan and add the chicken. Cook for 4 minutes per side.
4. Brush the chicken with the sauce, reduce the heat to low and cook for about 1,5 minutes. Flip the chicken and brush again with the sauce, and cook for about 1 minute. Reduce from the heat and set aside.
5. Add the rocket lettuce to a bowl and mix it with iceberg lettuce.
6. Add the chicken, orange, pomegranate, and pecan nuts. Top with the remaining sauce.

-200g boneless, skinless chicken breast, diced (7.0 oz)

-30g rocket lettuce (1.0 oz)

-¼ iceberg lettuce

-1 orange, peeled and divided

-¼ pomegranate, seeds divided

-50g pecan nuts, roughly chopped (1.8 oz)

For the sauce: (3 tbsp. honey + 2 tbsp. honey mustard + 1tbsp. extra virgin olive oil + 1 tbsp. lemon juice + 2 tbsp. orange juice + ¼ tsp. ground cinnamon)

Day 25

Today's breakfast will remind you of your sweet childhood. A pudding is something that everybody loves but not everybody can eat such a meal on a daily basis because it's usually high on calories. The Millet Pudding is so hearty and healthy that it will make your breakfast routine more joyful while being good for your body, not to mention it's super easy to prepare. The second meal will consist of Tuna & Broccoli Pasta, and it's going to meet your requirements for proteins and greens during the day. The last dish calls for the Shrimp & Tomatoes Thai Salad which is fancy, nutritious, and tastes like heaven.

Shrimp & Tomatoes Thai Salad

Millet Pudding

 2　 449　 15'

1. Rinse the millet thoroughly and place it in a pot. Add 250ml of milk, cover with a lid and bring to a boil. Cook for 15 minutes until the millet absorbs all the liquid.
2. Add another 250ml of milk along with the peanut butter and stir well to combine.
3. Pour the millet into a blender, add one half of banana, and mix until smooth.
4. Serve the millet in bowls. Add another half of banana, sprinkle with pomegranate, and top with the maple syrup.

-100g millet (3.5 oz)

-500ml almond milk (16.9 fl oz)

-2 tbsp. peanut butter

-1 banana

-½ pomegranate

-2 tbsp. maple syrup

Tuna & Broccoli Pasta

 2　 584　 7'

1. Cook the pasta al dente (4-5 minutes). Add the broccoli florets 2,5 minutes before removing the pasta.
2. Drain the pasta. Heat the olive oil in the empty pot and add the garlic. Sauté for 30 seconds.
3. Add the tomatoes, increase the heat, and add the chili flakes. Season with salt and pepper and cook for 1-2 minutes until the sauce thickens.
4. Stir in the pasta and broccoli. Gently fold in the tuna.
5. Serve the pasta in large plates and top with the mozzarella cheese.

-125g penne pasta (4.4 oz)

-2 tomatoes, blanched, peeled, and diced

-1 broccoli, cut into florets

-2 tbsp. extra virgin olive oil

-2 garlic cloves

-100g canned tuna (3.5 oz)

-10 balls of baby mozzarella

Shrimp & Tomatoes Thai Salad

 3　 350　 8'

1. Cook the noodles according to package directions (4-5 minutes) and cut them into smaller chunks.
2. Place the rice vinegar and sugar in a pot. Stir to combine and bring to a boil. Cook for about 1 minute and add the shrimps with the a half of the chili pepper.
3. Cook the shrimps for 1 minute per side. Remove from the heat.
4. Add the remaining chili, lime juice, and soy sauce. Stir well to combine.
5. Place the noodles in a bowl. Add the tomatoes, cucumber, and shrimps. Top with the sauce and garnish with peanuts and chives. Stir gently to combine all ingredients.

-100g soy noodles (3.5 oz)

-10 Black Tiger Shrimps, fresh or frozen

-150g cherry tomatoes, cut in halves (5.3 oz)

-40g cucumber, thinly sliced (1.4 oz)

-3 tbsp. peanuts

-1 rec chili pepper, finely chopped

-3 tbsp. chopped chives

For the sauce: (1 tbsp. freshly grated ginger + 80ml rice vinegar + ½ tbsp. soy sauce + 3 tbsp. lime juice + 2 tbsp. raw cane sugar)

Day 26

Another gluten-free and delicious breakfast is about to arrive at your table. Taste these Corn Pies with fried egg and you'll never say "no" to gluten-free meals. Another dish worth our attention when speaking of whole-food recipes is the Beef & Vegetables Chow Mein. There's this certain and immense charm in stir-fry meals, and this Chow Mein will make you sing songs of happiness for the rest of the day, speaking of which there's the Ricotta & Strawberries Salad for dinner. The combination of white Italian cheese with low-carb strawberries is a brilliant meal that tastes well both as a single dish and as an addition to grilled meat.

Beef & Vegetables Chow Mein

Corn Pies

 2   462   10'

1. Drain the corn kernels and mix them in a food processor with turmeric. Pulse the corn until relatively smooth, with small chunks of kernels visible on the surface.
2. In a large bowl, combine the corn mixture with basil, heavy cream, and egg. Add the baking soda, season with salt, and mix until well combined.
3. Heat the coconut oil in a large non-stick pan. Add 1 ½ tablespoon of the corn batter and level it to the 0.7-mm thickness. Cook 4 pies at a time for 1,5 minutes per side.
4. In the meantime, fry the eggs in a separate pre-heated pan for 3 minutes on medium heat.

-400g corn kernels (14.1 oz)
-2 eggs
-6 tbsp. cornstarch
-½ tsp. baking soda

-2 tbsp. heavy cream
-½ tsp. salt
-½ tsp. turmeric

-½ tsp. sweet paprika
-Fresh basil leaves
-Coconut oil for frying

Beef & Vegetables Chow Mein

 2   502   10'

1. Add the noodles to a pot with boiling water and cook them for 4 minutes. Rinse with cold water afterwards.
2. Heat the coconut oil in a wok. Add the garlic with ginger and sauté for 30 seconds.
3. Add the beef and sauté for 2 minutes until cooked through.
4. Add the leek, pepper, and mushrooms. Cook for 3 minutes, stirring constantly.
5. Stir in the noodles and season them with pepper. Pour in the soy sauce and water. Stir well to combine and cook for about 2 minutes.
6. Drizzle with sesame oil and sprinkle with chives.

-80g Chow Mein noodles (2.8 oz)
-170g beef sirloin, thinly sliced (6.0 oz)
-1 garlic clove
-1 tbsp. freshly grated ginger
-¼ leek, thinly sliced (only the light-green and white parts)

-½ red bell pepper, deseeded and cut in stripes
-3 mushrooms, sliced
-2 tbsp. coconut oil
-3 tbsp. light soy sauce

-2 tbsp. water
-2 tsp. sesame oil
-2 tbsp. chopped chives
-A pinch of white pepper

Ricotta & Strawberries Salad

 2   290   5'

1. In a medium saucepan, heat the balsamic vinegar and add the sugar. Stir until the sugar is dissolved. Remove from the heat and set aside.
2. Place the lettuce in a bowl. Add the avocado, season with salt, pepper, and drizzle with olive oil.
3. Add the ricotta cheese and strawberries
4. Season with salt, pepper, and toss with the balsamic sauce.

-100g iceberg lettuce (3.5 oz)
-1 ripe avocado, peeled, deseeded and diced

-200g strawberries, sliced (7.0 oz)
-125g ricotta cheese(4.4 oz)
-Salt and pepper to taste

For the balsamic sauce:
(2 tbsp. balsamic vinegar +
2 tbsp. raw cane sugar)

Day 27

These Apple & Cinnamon Oat Cookies are what people in good shape call Wake & Bake. Crispy on the outside and chewy inside, they can make even the most challenging day start with a generous pinch of happiness. The Chicken Caprese that you're going to have for lunch embraces what we love the most about Italy; tender meat, tomatoes, and fresh mozzarella cheese. The dinner will be, least to say, extraordinary, as the Cauliflower Pancakes are the new way of having your daily shot of veggies. Excited? Hungry? Check out this awesome meal plan with whole-foods recipe.

Chicken Caprese

Healthy Apple & Cinnamon Oat Cookies   4   310   15'

1. Preheat the oven to 170 degrees.
2. In a large bowl, combine instant oat flakes with flour, baking soda, cinnamon, and salt.
3. In a separate bowl, combine the egg with coconut oil and maple syrup. Add the dry ingredients and mix until well combined. Refrigerate for 5 minutes.
4. Add the apple to the cookie batter.
5. Spoon 1 tbsp. of the batter on a baking sheet and flatten them gently with a spatula.
6. Bake for 10-13 minutes.

-100g instant oat flakes(3.5 oz)
-90g whole-grain flour (3.2 oz)
-1 ½ tsp. baking soda

-1 ½ tsp. ground cinnamon
-1 pinch of salt
-2 tbsp. coconut oil

-1 tsp. vanilla extract
-110ml maple syrup (3.7 fl oz)
-1 apple, peeled and finely chopped

Chicken Caprese   2   496   7'

1. Season the chicken with salt, pepper, and dried oregano. Rub with olive oil and set aside.
2. Combine the tomatoes with the mozzarella cheese, and shallot. Season with salt and pepper.
3. Heat the grill pan on medium heat. Add the chicken breast fillets and cook for 3 minutes per side. Drizzle the meat with lemon juice before flipping.
4. Top the chicken with balsamic vinegar & maple syrup mixture. Serve on plates.
5. Garnish with the caprese salad.

-300g boneless skinless chicken breast fillets, cut in half lengthwise (10.6 oz)
-1 tbsp. dried oregano
-1 ½ tbsp. extra virgin olive oil
-1 tbsp. lemon juice

-1 tbsp. balsamic vinegar
-1 tsp. maple syrup
-250g cherry tomatoes, cut in halves (8.8 oz)
-100g fresh mozzarella cheese, sliced (3.5 oz)

-15g fresh basil leaves (0.5 oz)
-1 small shallot, finely chopped
-1 tsp. extra virgin olive oil for topping the salad

Cauliflower Pancakes   2   385   10'

1. Combine the cauliflower with the carrot and onion.
2. Add both flours, egg, salt, and black pepper. Season with the nutmeg and white pepper.
3. Heat the coconut oil in a large non-stick pan. Use 2 tbsp. of the cauliflower batter for 1 pancake. Cook the pancakes for 4 minutes per side until golden brown.

-300g cauliflower, roughly grated (10.6 oz)
-½ carrot, roughly grated
-¼ onion, finely grated

-3 tbsp. whole-grain flour
-2 tsp. potato flour
-1 egg

A pinch of each: salt, freshly ground black pepper, white pepper, nutmeg
-3 tbsp. coconut oil for frying

Day 28

Apple & Raisins Muesli is a classic, hearty, and juicy breakfast that is capable of blowing one's palate with the very first spoon, not to mention that they contain a controlled amount of simple sugars combined with some complex carbs to make your first dish fully nutritious. Your lunch will consist of Soy Noodles With Chicken & Vegetables. This meal can also be served vegetarian way by replacing the chicken with tofu or fried eggs. Speaking of vegetarian meals, you'll appreciate the Dried Tomatoes Tartar – a lightly condiment spread over a few slices of fresh, whole-grain bread. If you fancy dried tomatoes, this is going to be your No. 1 recipe.

Soy Noodles With Chicken & Vegetables

Apple & Raisins Muesli

 2 416 7'

1. Boil the water in a pot. Add oat flakes and cook them for 5 minutes.
2. Drain the oat flakes and set them aside.
3. In the meantime, add the apple to a medium bowl. Drizzle with lemon juice, top with maple syrup, and season with cinnamon. Stir until well combined
4. Combine the oat flakes with the apple mixture and natural yoghurt.

-54g instant oat flakes(1.9 oz)

-2 tbsp. raisins

-500ml water (16.9 fl oz)

-1 apple, peeled and diced

-1 tbsp. lemon juice

-1 tbsp. maple syrup

-1/3 tsp. cinnamon

-75g natural yoghurt (2.6 oz)

Soy Noodles With Chicken & Vegetables

 3 300 10'

1. Pour water over the noodles and set aside for 5 minutes. Drain them and cut into smaller chunks.
2. In the meantime, heat the coconut oil in a wok. Add the ginger with garlic and sauté for 30 seconds until fragrant.
3. Add the chicken and cook for about 5 minutes, stirring constantly.
4. Add the carrot and sauté for a minute. After that, add mushrooms and red bell pepper. Cook for about 5 minutes, stirring from time to time.
5. Add the corn kernels and Chinese cabbage. Season with white pepper, add the chopped chili, and cook for 3 minutes.
6. Stir in the noodles. Add the soy sauce mixture and bring to a boil. Cook for 2 minutes.
7. Garnish with chives and stir well to combine.

-150g soy vermicelli noodles (5.3 oz)

-2 tsp. coconut oil

-1 tsp. freshly grated ginger

-2 garlic cloves, finely grated

-250g boneless, skinless chicken breast, diced (8.8 oz)

-1 carrot, finely grated

-½ red bell pepper, diced

-100g Chinese cabbage (3.5 oz)

-150g mushrooms (5.3 oz)

-4 tbsp. corn kernels

-½ tsp. white pepper

-½ red chili pepper, finely chopped

-4 tbsp. chopped chives

For the sauce: (60ml light soy sauce

+ 1 tbsp. raw cane sugar

+ 2 tbsp. rice vinegar)

Dried Tomatoes Tartare

 4 150 12'

1. Heat a grill pan and add the zucchini. Cook for 5 minutes per side. Remove from the heat, drizzle with olive oil and season with the thyme.
2. Add the tomatoes and onion to a food processor. Pulse until mixed in small chunks. Add the zucchini and pulse again until finely mixed.
3. Add the balsamic and wine vinegar, salt, pepper, tabasco sauce, and chives. Mix once more for a few seconds.
4. Spread the tomato tartare over the bread.

-1 small zucchini, sliced

-2 tbsp. extra virgin olive oil

-A pinch of dried thyme

-90g dried tomatoes (3.2 oz)

-1 shallot, chopped

-1 tsp. red wine vinegar

-1 tsp. balsamic vinegar

-2-3 drops of tabasco sauce

-2 tbsp. chopped chives

-4 slices of whole-grain bread for serving

-Salt and pepper to taste

Day 29

Day 29 is rich in fish and vegetables. For breakfast, you're going to indulge yourself in vegan Hummus Wraps with a generous portion of vegetables to take care of your greens. Lunch is where fish enter the game. A tender, almost mouth meltingly cod meat covered in red pesto is what every fish fan will savour. The dinner, we're going to switch from cooking to grilling, as the Grilled Salmon Salad will rule the plate. Nutritious and refreshing, this salad is one hell of a reason to fall asleep with a big smile on your face.

Cod Fillets With Red Pesto

Hummus Wraps

 2   407   10'

1. Heat a grill pan and add the zucchini. Cook 5 minutes per side over medium heat. Season with a pinch of oregano and drizzle with olive oil. Set aside.
2. Spread the hummus over tortillas and add the zucchini, lettuce, and tomatoes. Season with freshly ground pepper and roll the wraps.

-2 whole-grain tortillas

-4 tbsp. hummus

-1 small zucchini, sliced

-1 tomato, sliced and seasoned with salt

-1 handful of lettuce

-Salt, pepper, oregano, and olive oil to taste

Cod Fillets With Red Pesto

 2   385   15'

1. Season the cod fillets with salt and pepper.
2. Place the potatoes in a pot. Cover with water and bring to a boil. Cook until soft.
3. Prepare the pesto: place the cherry tomatoes, dried tomatoes, garlic, and chili paste in a saucepan. Season with salt and pepper, and cook for about 3 minutes. Add the basil and mix with a blender until smooth.
4. Add the cod fillets to the pot with pesto and cook under a lid for 4-5 minutes. Flip the fish in the middle of cooking.
5. Serve on the potato puree.

-200g cod fillets (7.0 oz)

-200g potatoes, peeled and diced (7.0 oz)

-180g cherry tomatoes (6.3 oz)

-3 dried tomatoes

-2 garlic cloves

-2 tbsp. extra virgin olive oil

-½ tsp. chili paste (optional)

-10 fresh basil leaves

Grilled Salmon Salad

 2   437   10'

1. Cut the salmon into 1,5cm stripes. Season with salt and pepper, and rub with the olive oil.
2. Grill the salmon in a pan, 5 minutes per side. Rub with the maple syrup and cook for 1 minute until golden-brown.
3. Mix all ingredients of the salad. Add the yoghurt, mint, and stir well to combine.
4. Top with the salmon and season with salt and pepper.

-250g salmon (8.8 oz)

-1 tsp. olive oil

-1 tsp. maple syrup (optional)

-½ head of iceberg lettuce, shredded

-½ cucumber, peeled and diced

-1 tomato, diced

-2 shallots, chopped

-30g fresh mint leaves, chopped (1.0 oz)

-180g natural yoghurt (6.3 oz)

-Salt and pepper to taste

Day 30

Welcome to the last day of our adventure with whole-foods recipes. You'd better get ready for some super quick and, as always, delicious cooking with products of top-notch quality. Today, we're going to make a fusion of tradition and extravagance for breakfast. Our Guacamole Stuffed Eggs will rock your plates until the very last bite with their Mexican topping. Lunch, on the other hand, is a journey to Italy, where you'll savour the flavours of green beans and pancetta in the Green Beans & Pancetta Salad With Leek. In order to finish our 30-day plan with something out of space, we have prepared the Watermelon Pizza with feta and black olives topping, because why not?

Guacamole Stuffed Eggs

Guacamole Stuffed Eggs

 3   224   10'

1. Bring water to a boil in a medium pot. Hard boil the eggs for 8-10 minutes and place them in a cold water until cooled. Remove the shells and cut the egg in halves lengthwise.
2. Divide the yolks from the whites and mash them with a fork.
3. Mash the avocado, drizzle with olive oil, and combine with egg yolks.
4. Add the garlic, tabasco sauce, olive, and cilantro. Season with salt and pepper.
5. Add the tomato and stir gently to combine.
6. Stuff the egg whites with guacamole and garnish with chives.

-5 large eggs

-1 ripe avocado, peeled and deseeded

-1 tbsp. lime juice

-½ garlic clove, grated

-4 drops of tabasco sauce

-2 tsp. extra virgin olive oil

-2 tbsp. chopped cilantro leaves

-1 tbsp. chopped chives

-1 small tomato, finely diced

Beans & Pancetta Salad

 2   384   10'

1. Rinse the beans and cut off the hard parts.
2. In a large pot, bring water to a boil. Add beans and cook for 4-5 minutes until al dente.
3. In the meantime, sauté the pancetta and add the sliced leek. Cook for 2-3 minutes until the leek is soft. If there's not enough fat on the saucepan, you can add 1-2 tablespoons of olive oil.
4. Season the leek and pancetta with salt and add the pumpkin seeds with garlic. Stir in the drained beans and heat up for a minute.
5. Season with salt and pepper to taste.

-300g young green beans (10.6 oz)

-80g pancetta, chopped (2.8 oz)

-1 leek (only the green and white parts), sliced

-2 tbsp. olive oil

-3 tbsp. pumpkin seeds

-1 garlic clove, grated

-2 tbsp. chopped parsley

-Salt and pepper to taste

Watermelon "Pizza"

 3   333   5'

1. Wash the watermelon and cut it into 1,5-cm thick slices. Divide each slice into 6 equal pieces.
2. Sprinkle with crumbled feta cheese and olive oils. Garnish with mint leaves.
3. Drizzle the "pizza" with a mixture of 1 tbsp. lime juice and 1 tbsp. maple syrup.

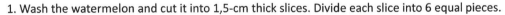

-1 medium watermelon, sliced

-100g feta cheese (3.5 oz)

-A handful of black olives, sliced

-A handful of fresh mint leaves

-Maple syrup and lime juice for garnish

Warm Up Exercises

Welcome to the 30 day Whole Exercise challenge. Here you will find the detailed list of exercises to perform each day, and after this listed exercise you will find each exercise detailed with pictures. One of the most important parts of this exercise challenge are the warm up routines. Make sure every time before your exercise routing you do this warm-up exercises to avoid injury.

Lower Body

Jumping jacks - 60 seconds

High knees - 45 seconds

Butt kicks - 30 seconds

High kicks - 30 seconds

Forward lunges - 30 seconds

Side lunges - 30 seconds

Upper Body

Jumping jacks - 30 seconds

Forward arm circles -- 20 seconds

Backwards arm circles -- 20 seconds

Arm crossovers - 30 seconds

Shoulder circle shrugs - 15 reps

Side bends - 10 reps each side

Week One

Let's dip right into the first week of this 30 whole exercise days. Take it easy and follow the steps given in the next section of the book "exercises" to avoid injury or mistakes. Never forget warming up before starting. As it is the first week, the resting time between sets is free. Take your time to recover y our breath, but do not wait long enough to cool down excessively. If you ever find an exercise is too hard, just reduce the number of repetitions to something you find comfortable with.

Monday

Squat Jumps	Calf raises
Walking lunges	Single leg deadlift
Hamstring curls	

Tuesday

Triceps dips	Planks
Scapula pushups	Leg raises

Wednesday

Jump Squats	Bulgarian split squats
Hamstring curls	Superman

Thursday

Triceps dips	Leg raises
Scapula pushups	Planks

Friday

Squat Jumps	Calf raises
Walking lunges	Single leg dead lift
Wall sits	

Saturday

Pushups	Bicycle
Scapula pushups	Toe touchers

Week Two

As we get into week 2 things start getting slightly more difficult with the number of exercises increasing. This week we will try to set a maximum resting time between sets of 60 seconds. Try to comply with it, but should you not be able do not worry, wait as long as needed. At this point you should feel more agile and energetic.

Monday

Jump Squats	Leg raise
Step up	Calf raises
Superman	

Tuesday

Scapula push ups	Mountain climbers
Reverse snow angles	Flutter kicks
	Triceps dips

Wednesday

Jump Squats	Step up
Walking lunges	Flutter kicks
	Calf raises

Thursday

Inclined pushups	Scapula pushup
Diamond pushups	Romanian twist
Plank	Bicycle

Friday

Jump Squats	Wall Sits
Step up	Calf raises
Hamstring curls	

Saturday

Scapula pushups	Planks
	Triceps dips
Diamond pushups	Romanian kicks

Week Three

We are just past the equator of the 30 days whole exercise challenge. If you feel strong, we recommend you decreasing the resting time between sets to 45 seconds. But if you ever feel too tired or sore you can increase that time. Moreover, if a particular day you feel really sore, skip one or two exercises or add an extra resting day all together.

Monday

Jumps Squats	Walking lunges
Calf raises	Hamstring curls
Superman	

Tuesday

Pushups	Scapula pushups
Triceps dips	
Leg raises	Planks

Wednesday

Jump Squats	Hamstring curls
Bulgarian split squats	Superman
	Calf raises

Thursday

Diamond pushups	Ab crunches
Scapula pushups	Mountain Climbers
Bicycle	Side planks

Friday

Squat Jumps	Calf raises
Walking lunges	Single leg deadlift
Wall sits	

Saturday

Scapula Pushups	Bicycle
	Toe touchers
Diamond Pushups	Triceps dips

Week Four

As we get closer to the end, things get even harder: Aim now to rest no more than 30 seconds between repetitions. Again never force yourself beyond what you feel safe.The amount of exercises stays stable and by now you should definitely feel stronger and if you hove followed the diet, not only leaner but with enhanced levels of energy. Corry on like this!

Monday

Jump Squats	Step up
Superman	Single leg hip bridge
Calf raises	

Tuesday

Scapula pushups	Flutter kicks
Triceps dips	Mountain climbers
Romanian Twists	

Wednesday

Jumping Squats	Step up
Calf raises	Flutter kicks
Walking lunges	Bulgarian split squats

Thursday

Toe-Touchers	Romanian twist
Scapula pushups	Triceps Dips
	Plank

Friday

Jump Squats	Glute bridge
Step up	Calf raises
Hamstring curls	

Saturday

Jump Squats	Hamstring curls
Bulgarian split squats	Superman
	Calf raises

The Last Push

If you have made it this far and stayed consistent with both this exercise schedule and diet, congratulations: by now you must be a completely different person. You will feel rejuvenated and extremely more energetic, with a noticeably improved force of will and capacity of focus. Maintain your rest between repetitions at 30 seconds and finish this program off!

Monday

Jump Squats	Single leg hip bridge
Step up	
superman	Calf raises

Tuesday

Diamond pushups	Ab crunches
Scapula pushups	Mountain Climbers
Side planks	Bicycle

Single leg Deadlift

Preparation

a. Place your feet hip-width apart with your toes pointing forward.
b. Place your arms by your sides and keep your arms extended with you elbows just slightly bent.
c. If using resistance, grab a hold of the dumbbell or kettlebell with your palms in a neutral position with the palms facing in.

The exercise

1. Begin the exercises by extending and elevating your left leg behind you as you drop your shoulders over your toes.
2. Try to reach the left leg behind you while keeping your left knee stationary.
3. Once you have descended low enough to touch the top of the platform or to the point you can no longer keep your spine in a neural position, exhale to raise yourself back to the starting position.

Exercise tips

Give yourself the best chance to succeed by starting in an efficient standing position with your head tall, shoulders back, and chest out. Try starting with your dominant side to use as your initial stance leg in order to be able to maintain your balance. Follow these steps for the most benefit:

1. If starting on your right leg, push your right toe into the ground to keep your feet firm on the ground.
2. Extend your left elevated leg behind you while keep it aligned with your straight torso.
3. Gently touch the top of a platform or reach your extended arms to maximum depth of your mid shin before exhaling back to the starting position

 3x10 rep   **4x10 reps**   **4x12 reps**

We all at some point have lost our balance or have displayed un-athleticism while attempting to keep our feet underneath us either on a dance floor or simply stepping off a curb. The single leg deadlift retrains your body to be able to elegantly transfer your weight into a single leg stance resembling that of the most adept stork stance. Other benefits include: Reducing lower back pain, Strengthen your glutes and hamstrings, Improve asymmetry between your left and right leg

Jump Squats

Preparation

a. Place your feet hip-width apart with your toes pointing forward.
b. Place your arms by your sides and keep your arms extended with you elbows just slightly bent.
c. Imagine straightening your body alignment by raising.

The exercise

1. Begin the exercise by hinging your hips slightly backward and allowing your knees to track outward and slightly over your second toe.
2. Drop your hips until you've reached a depth where you are no longer able to maintain a neutral spine while extending your arms behind you.
3. Explode up by quickly extending your legs to propel yourself off the ground while swinging arms up overhead.
4. Be sure to absorb the impact by bending your hips and knees as you come back into contact with the ground.

Exercise tips

Place an equal distribution of your body weight throughout your feet and keeping your heels planted will ensure you do not become off balanced. Be sure to exhale your breath as you begin the jump while maintaining a braced core by exhaling through parse lips.

1. Land with your feet directly underneath your hips in order to maintain your center of gravity upon impact.
2. Land on the balls of your feet as the initial form of contact in order efficiently transfer the forces caused by the jump.

 3x8 rep   **3x10 reps**   **3x12 reps**

It's inevitable that on multiple occasions throughout the day we are repeatedly required to squat in order to complete daily tasks. The squat to jump exercise enables you to strengthen a movement that is so influential to vitality it is arguably the most performed movement pattern during the day. Other benefits include: Improving range of motion in your hips, knees, and ankles, Building bone density through a plyometric exercise, Improving athleticism and power through quick movements.

Scapula push up

Preparation

a. Keep your arms extended and only have movement through the shoulders.
b. Avoid shrugging your shoulders and keeping them relaxed.

The exercise

1. Squeeze your shoulder blades together to bring your chest forward between your arms while avoiding any bending in the elbows.
2. Separate your shoulder blades by rounding them around your upper back to bring your chest away from the wall.
3. Once this movement has been established, progress the exercise by making your body more horizontal to the ground by either using an elevated platform or dropping completely to the ground.

Exercise tips

Understanding proper mechanics of the shoulder will dramatically decrease your risk of injury and improve overall posture. If you have developed a hunched posture, you may need to routinely stretch out your chest on top of performing the scapula push up. This will regain balance between the muscles and position your shoulder blades back to the optimal position. Other tips include:

1. Imagining squeezing a piece of paper between the shoulder blades when you are flexing them together.
2. Trying to push your shoulder blades away from your body when trying to round them around your upper back.

 3x10 rep   **3x12 reps**   **3x15 reps**

It's become a known epidemic that our posture has become distorted from sedentary lifestyle, inefficient repetitive movements, and poor ergonomics. The scapula pushup allows you to combat poor posture and build the strength and endurance your shoulder blades need to keep you in tall, confident posture. Other benefits include: Improved shoulder girdle health, correcting muscle imbalances in the shoulder and increased shoulder range of motion.

Single leg hip bridge

Preparation

a. Start Lying flat on the floor, bending your right knee so that the heel is planted firmly on the ground while bending and elevating your left leg off the floor.
b. Rest your arms on the ground about 45 degrees from your torso with your palms facing down.
c. Rotate your pelvis slightly upward to allow your back to become flush with the floor.
d. Brace your core by taking a deep breath into your stomach and flexing the abdominal muscles like a corset around the breath.

The exercise

1. From this position, press through your right heel while contracting the same side glute to elevate your hips.
2. Continue the extension for your hips until you have made a straight alignment from your shoulders to your right knee.
3. Slowly lower yourself back to the floor and repeat the steps with the opposite leg.

Exercise tips

As you progressively increase strength you can implement resistance to improve the difficulty of the exercise.

1. By elevating your heel you will cause an increased range of motion requirement that places more physical stress on the body.
2. You may use a plyo box or a step that is positioned about 1 foot in front of your hips. Other forms of increasing the difficulty can be to add a barbell by positioning it over your upper thighs.
3. Be sure to properly progress the single leg glute-bridge before jumping into the most difficult version.

 3x8 rep   **3x12 reps**   **3x15 reps**

It's a thing of envy to view a pair of powerful glutes that can squat even the most demanding weight. The glutes serve as the main component in hip extension that is required not only for squatting, but simply standing up out of our chair. The single leg hip bridge hones in on developing power, strength, as well as contributes to a pleasing aesthetic appearance. The variations in difficulty this exercise can offer and the numerous benefits it possesses make it a needed staple in anybody's fitness regime.

Reverse snow angle

Preparation

a. Begin the reverse snow angel exercise by lying onto your stomach with your feet spread to shoulder-width apart and your toes tucked underneath your heels. You can use a folded towel or a pillow to rest your forehead on.
b. Extend your arms by your sides with your palms facing the floor. Your toes should be in contact with the floor throughout the exercise

The exercise

1. Elevate your palms and forehead above the floor by rolling your shoulders back.
2. Keep your palms elevated as you begin making a snow angel by arching your arms out wide.
3. Continue the arch until your arms are extended overhead.
4. Keep the movement controlled as you reverse the arch back to the starting position.
5. Continue with more repetitions as long as you are to execute it flawlessly.

Exercise tips

Due to the fact that not everybody is going to be able to have perfectly positioned shoulder blades due to the overactivity and tightness from the front of the torso, you may need to spend some time warming up before jumping into the reverse snow angle. Some quick exercises to do before the reverse snow angel could be:

- Wall slides
- Hanging door stretch
- Cat to camel
- Doorway chest stretch

These exercises can loosen any inhibiting tightness through the thoracic spine, lats, and chest.

 3x30 rep　　　 **3x45 reps**　　　 **3x60 reps**

Poor posture can cause numerous complications such as the wear and tear on the muscles and joints associated with the dysfunctional areas. Intently strengthening the smaller postural muscles will not only keep you from a devastating injury, but allow you to exude confidence by standing tall and showcasing healthy shoulders. This can all be accomplished by performing a user friendly exercise known as the reverse snow angel to exasperate scapula tightness and keep you standing tall.

Step ups

Preparation

a. Stand in a tall posture, feet hip-width apart, arms at your sides, and facing a step, or plyo box, 3 to 6 inches in front of you

b. It is of absolute importance that you stand far enough back so that when you perform the step up, you do not catch your feet on the side of the step and become off balanced.

The Exercise

1. Shift your weight to the left leg in order to lift your right leg up over the step and plant it firmly on top of the deck

2. Shift weight now into your right leg in order to raise your left leg off the floor and on top of the deck next to your right foot

3. Reverse the order you came up with until you are back to the starting position.

Exercise tips

When using dumbbells, keep your arms extended and palms facing your body as you hold onto the dumbbells. You can also place a barbell on the base of your neck to add additional difficulty. Keep an upright torso by: Bracing your core, stepping onto the box heel first and driving through the heel to raise you back leg and exhaling through pursed lips as you step onto the deck of the box.

 3x12 rep   **3x15 reps**   **3x18 reps**

One of the most functionally rewarding exercises is the step up exercise. Not only are you able to isolate a single leg and acquire the same benefits from a two legged squat, but you perform a movement that greatly enhances your livelihood. How many steps having you taken today? My guess is at least one. Other benefits include: Improving symmetrical strength through both legs, developing hip power, improving balance by shifting your body weight from leg to leg, increasing muscular endurance

Plank

Preparation

a. Elbows underneath your shoulders.
b. Forearms parallel with each other.
c. Palms facing down.

The Exercise

1. Shift your weight to the left leg in order to lift your right leg up over the step and plant it firmly on top of the deck.
2. Once your arms are in this position, bring your feet together and tuck your toes underneath your heels
3. Take a deep breath to brace your core before elevating your knees and hips above the floor keeping your body in a straight alignment from your heels to your shoulders.
4. Continue to breath into your stomach and exhale through parse lips in order to avoid losing your brace and sagging your lower back.
5. As a prerequisite exercise too much more challenging variations, you should aim for being able to hold this rigid straight alignment for a time of 30 seconds before advancing your exercise.

Exercise tips

If you have not yet built up enough strength to be able to hold this plank position there are modifications that can be made to instill sufficient strength in the core. The simplest way to modify this would be to rather than lifting your knees off the floor, keep them on the ground and make the straight alignment from your knees up to your shoulders. If you were able to hold this position without even the slightest movement than you are ready to advance to exercises such as: Ab roller, Inchworms, plank with arm extensions or plank with arm extensions and leg raise.

| EASY | **3x30 rep** | MEDIUM | **3x45 reps** | HARD | **3x60 reps** |

Starting a workout regime can be difficult at times and sometimes one becomes clueless on where to start. Imagine throwing a pebble into a lake and watching the ripples start right around the rock and the progress outward. This is the thought process to keep in mind when beginning a workout regime where you need to start with your core, the pebble, before moving outward. You may begin working on your core with a stable exercise known as the plank.

Leg raise

Preparation

a. Shift your weight to the left leg in order to lift your right leg up over the step and plant it firmly on top of the deck.
b. Begin breathing into your stomach and flexing your abdominal muscles around your deep inhale like tightening a corset.
c. Keep your legs extended with your knees slightly bent to allow proper blood flow.
d. Rotate your pelvis slightly upward to keep your lower back flush with the floor.
e. Keep your ankles flexed to 90 degrees to draw some strength from the flexion.

The Exercise

1. Take a deep inhale and flex your abdominal wall as you begin to raise your heels off the ground.
2. Continue to raise your legs until you have reached a vertical alignment.
3. Slowly lower your legs back to the starting position and continue for an allotted repetitions.

Exercise tips

If having a difficult time keeping your lower back flush with the floor, you can artificially add extra core stability by involving a resistance band. This is done by:

1. Anchoring the middle of the resistance band to a stationary, stable object.
2. Placing your head 2-3 feet away from that object.
3. Grabbing the handles with a double overhand grip.
4. Extending the handles to your hips a couple inches off the floor and keeping them in this position throughout the exercise.

 3x12 rep   **3x15 reps**   **3x18 reps**

The spine is designed to withstand excessive flexion and extension during even the most demanding times. It requires the assistance of your abdominal muscles to hold it into place to keep your spine happy and injury free. An exercise that allows you to challenge the positioning of the spine while making your abdominal muscles put in overtime to make sure the spine remains in a neutral position is an exercise known as the leg raise.

Calf raises

Preparation

a. Dip underneath the shoulder pads to rest them on your shoulders
b. Step onto the platform and positioning the balls of your feet, or your forefoot, securely on top of the platform while hanging your heels off the back
c. Stand in a tall upright position keeping your legs extended with the knees slightly bent

The Exercise

1. You can increase the range of motion by slightly dropping your heels towards the floor or keeping the soles of your feet parallel with the floor.
2. Once you have chosen your foot position, extend your ankles to raise your heels until you can no longer extend your ankles.
3. Controllably return to the starting position and repeat for allotted repetitions.

Exercise tips

The calf raise exercises is often considered a secondary exercise in that is should not be performed at the beginning of the workout. For that reason, it is often performed following larger compound movements such as squats or leg presses.

When performing the calf raise, you can alter the tempo, repetition range, or rest periods between sets to accommodate for your certain goals. If looking to increase size, perform more repetitions with lower rest time between sets or build strength by decreasing your repetitions and allowing more time between sets.

 3x15 rep   **4x15 reps**   **5x15 reps**

The world of bodybuilding requires strategic isolation of muscle groups in order to force them into hypertrophy. Muscles will not grow unless you place enough stress on them requiring them to adapt to added demands and creating more muscle fibers to accommodate the stress. A troublesome area for many weight lifters and aspiring bodybuilders is the calf muscle and there is no better way to force them into growth than with the calf raise exercises.

Triceps dips

Preparation

a. Standing upright on top of the step platforms of the hanging leg raise machine.
b. If there are no step platforms, bring a step over and place it in front of the machine
c. Grab ahold of the parallel bars with extended arms, elbows slightly bent, and an overhand grip so your palms are facing in.

The Exercise

1. From here you can place your weight through your palms to suspend your body above the ground allowing your knees to bend behind you.
2. Allow your torso to slightly lean forward in order to keep your shoulders back and chest up.
3. Descend your body to the ground by bending your elbows.
4. Keep your forearms vertical to the ground as you descend.
5. Drop to a deep enough depth to allow your upper arms to become parallel with the floor.

Exercise tips

The tricep dip can be modified to increase or decrease its difficulty. Many gyms offer an assisted dip machine that allows you to rest your knees on a pad and set the weight that will increase the assistance. You can also increase the tricep dip by wearing a dip belt that allows you to place additional resistance to the exercise. Keep your elbows angled to your torso and you will target more of the chest, where if you are targeting the triceps, you will need to keep your elbows close to your sides.

 3x10 rep   4x10 reps   4x15 reps

If you've ever been in the presence of a gymnast you immediately notice the low body fat and and a muscular frame that many aspiring bodybuilders strive for. Yet you rarely will see a gymnast performing curls or crunches so how do they build such a muscular physique? The secret lies in mastering your bodyweight movements and placing yourself in challenging positions with gravity as your resistance. One of the ways to begin implementing this strategy is through an exercise known as the triceps dip.

Wall sits

Preparation

a. Standing upright with your feet at shoulder-width apart about a foot away from the wall

b. Press your back against the wall keeping your lower back, shoulders, and back of your head against it at all times

The Exercise

1. Descend towards the ground and reposition yourself by keeping your thighs so that they are parallel with the floor
2. Your heels should be directly underneath your knees so step forward or back to assure this position.
3. Your hands should not be resting on your thighs to add additional support.
4. Holding this position will cause fatigue in your glutes, hamstrings, and quadriceps.

Be sure to continuously breathe as you inhale in through your nose into your stomach and exhale through parse lips to ensure you are keeping tension in your abdominal muscles.

Exercise tips

The wall sit exercise will quickly deplete your body's energy stores making it difficult to hold the contraction. If you are looking to increase the difficulty without having to increase the time, you do have the option of adding a barbell plate for additional resistance. To do this, you will need to place the barbell plate on top of your parallel thighs as close to your hips as possible. If increasing the difficulty by adding the barbell plate to the exercise, be sure to restart with being able to comfortably hold the wall sit for 30 seconds before increasing the time.

 3x30 rep   **3x45 reps**   **3x60 reps**

Isometric exercises allow you to continuously contract muscle groups to increase endurance and strength. The added benefit is that by performing an isometric exercise you are able to force the targeted muscle group to become active where they may normally be dormant and unresponsive. One of the most well-known isometric exercises to make sure your glutes, hamstrings, and quads are firing to their full potential, is the exercise known as the wall sit.

Bulgarian split squat

Preparation

c.   With your back to a bench 1-3 feet away
d.   Extend one leg behind you and place the top of the forefoot onto the bench
e.   Position your front heel underneath your front knee
f.   Keep your torso upright throughout the exercise
g.   Brace your core to sustain stability by inhaling into your stomach and flexing your abdominal wall against the inhaled air.

The Exercise

1. Descend your back knee to the floor keeping your front knee stationary.
2. Do not let your back foot move from it's original position.
3. Continue to descend until your back knee has reached just above the floor.

When raising back to the starting position, your body may want to sway forward to compensate for lack of strength. Be sure to continue inhaling into your stomach and exhaling through parse lips to keep your torso upright as you raise to the starting position.

Exercise tips

The bulgarian split squat will challenge your stability and balance so you will need to begin the exercise without added additional resistance until you're able to perform the movement without faltering your balance. If using dumbbells, you will perform the exercise with the dumbbells resting at your sides. If using a barbell, you will set the bench, or the plyo box, up close to a squat rack in order to rest the barbell on the base of the back of your neck.

| EASY | 3x10 rep | MEDIUM | 4x10 reps | HARD | 4x12 reps |

Hearing the names of foreign countries such as Romanian, Bulgarian, or Turkish placed before the name of an exercise should give you the immediate impression that the exercise is going to be challenging. The Romanians and Bulgarians have founded many challenging exercises that have allowed a fitness regime to go from sub-par to elite. One of those exercises that has taken a regular split squat and advanced it to supreme level is an exercise known as the Bulgarian split squat.

Walking lunge

Preparation

a. Stand upright with your feet shoulder width apart.
b. Equally distributing your weight throughout each foot.
c. Toes facing forward.
d. Chest up and shoulders back.
e. Inhale into your stomach and flex your abdominal wall against the inhaled air to keep your spine in an upright neutral position.

The Exercise

1. Strike heel first before planting your foot on the ground.
2. Descend the back knee towards to ground while lifting the back heel up.
3. Descend the back knee to just above the floor so that both your knees are bent to 90 degrees.
4. Push off the back foot and bring it to the front before repeating the steps for an allotted repetition range or distance.

Exercise tips

The walking lunge is a simple yet challenging exercise that can be advanced through the use of a barbell or dumbbells for added resistance. If using dumbbells, you will need to grab them in an overhand grip so that your palms are facing in and keep them rested by your hips. If you begin to have to sway your body forward to raise yourself off the ground, reduce the weight of the dumbbells.

 3x10 rep   **4x10 reps**   **5x10 reps**

Increasing speed, power, and strength require the body to become efficient at transferring forces and becoming as symmetrical as possible between your left and right sides. To improve your athletic ability, you will need to enhance movement through exercises that promote proper mechanics. One of those exercises that can not only improve speed, power, and strength, but also allow you to get a good sweat and great workout is the exercise known as the walking lunge.

Superman

Preparation

a. Keeping your heels extended and toes pointed throughout the exercise.
b. Extending your legs with slight flexion in your knees to prevent restriction in blood flow.
c. Arms overhead with your palms facing the floor and biceps by your ears.
d. You will also need to brace your core by inhaling in through your nose into your stomach and flexing your abdominal muscles around the inhaled air to keep your posture rigid.

The Exercise

1. Elevate your arms and chest off the ground by flexing below your shoulder blades and lower back.
2. You will notice that your muscles will quickly become fatigued holding this elevated posture. Work on performing quality reps without separating your feet and keeping your biceps by your ears.
3. Once you have held for an allotted time, exhale to lower your arms and legs back to the ground.

Exercise tips

Once you have developed enough strength and endurance to hold your feet together and biceps by your ears throughout the exercise, you are can then implement added resistance to make the exercise even more challenging. You can implement dumbbells to fatigue your middle and lower back by having to contract to hold up the added weight. You can do this by grabbing ahold of the dumbbells in a double overhand grip with your palms facing the ground.

 3x12 rep 4x15 reps 5x15 reps

Imagine staring up in the sky and noticing a flying man in a blue suite darting across the skyline. He'd be in the most efficient posture to become aerodynamic by pointing his toes behind him and his arms extended straight ahead with a little extension in his spine to keep everything straight. It is no surprise that there has been an exercise named after the super hero superman and it is also no surprise that the exercise builds a superhuman posture by strengthening the lower back.

Bicycle

Preparation

a. Extending your legs on the ground allowing your knees to be slightly flexed.
b. Placing your hands behind your head without clasping your hands. You will instead, gently touch the back of head with your fingertips.
c. Keep your ankles flexed to 90 degrees
d. Rotate your pelvis upward to place your lower back flush against the ground
e. From this position you will raise your heels off the ground making a 90 degree angle with your right knee and positioning your right thigh vertical to the ground.
f. Extend your left leg out hovering your heel above the floor 2 to 3 inches.

The Exercise

1. Flex the bottom of your ribcage into your belly button to lift your shoulders off the floor.
2. Bring your right knee up towards your chest and rotate your shoulders so you touch your right knee with your left elbow.
3. Keep the movement continuous and fluent as you extend your right leg and bring the left knee up towards your chest.
4. Rotate your shoulders to touch your right elbow to your left knee.

Exercise tips

The bicycle exercise can have increased difficulty by either increasing the repetitions or increasing the time as it causes fatigue in your abdominal muscles quickly. If you are wanting to increase the exercise without increasing the time or repetitions, you can add additional resistance with a pair of ankle weights. The ankle weights will cause your legs to fatigue as well as place additional stress on your abdominal muscles as move the legs in and out.

EASY **3x10 rep**   MEDIUM **3x15 reps**   HARD **3x20 reps**

A strong core allows you to move in different body positions while being able to maintain a neutral spine to reduce stressful forces. There has been many abdominal exercises created to strengthen the core with variations in difficulty by either staying stationary or becoming dynamic. The dynamic category in most advance that allows you to go through movement and challenge your abdominal muscles. An exercise that provides the dynamic component while greatly strengthening your core is an exercise known as the bicycle.

Mountain climber

Preparation

a. Place your hands shoulder-width apart directly underneath your shoulders.
b. Tuck your toes underneath your heels
c. Brace your core by inhaling in through your nose and into the stomach by flexing your abdominal wall against the inhaled air to keep your spine neutral throughout the exercise.
d. Raise your knees off the ground making a straight alignment from your heels up to your shoulders.

The Exercise

1. Flexing your right knee up towards your chest allowing your hips to raise slightly.
2. Quickly return your right leg to the starting position before quickly raising your left knee you towards your chest.
3. Continue repeatedly flexing your right then your left knee up to your chest for an allotted time.

Exercise tips

The mountain climber can be challenging to begin and so may require the use of either gliders or a bench or plyo box to get the movement down before advancing to just your body weight. If using a bench or plyo box, you will start with the same straight body alignment from your heels up to your shoulders. You will still keep your hands underneath your shoulders except you will have your hands placed on the bench or plyo box to make the exercise easier.

 3x30 rep   **3x45 reps**   **3x60 reps**

Plyometric exercises serves many benefits including increase cardiorespiratory endurance, increased bone density, improved athleticism, and increased ability to burn fat. Exercises including, bounding, leaping, or continuous quick repetitions will build endurance, speed, and power that carries over into every aspect of your life. An exercise that not only gives the added benefit of speed, power, and endurance, but also gives you the added benefit of stabilizing your core is an exercise known as the mountain climber.

Flutter Kicks

Preparation

a. Extending your legs keeping your knees slightly bent to ensure proper blood flow.
b. b .Extending your arms by your sides with your palms facing the floor.
a. Rotating your pelvis upward to allow your lower back to be flush against the floor.
b. Bracing your core to keep your lower back from raising off the floor by inhaling into your stomach through your nose into your stomach and flexing your abdominal wall against the inhaled air.
c. Try to imagine stretching your spine out to keep your torso stationary throughout the exercise.

The Exercise

1. Elevate your left leg so that the heel is 2 to 3 inches off of the floor
2. Elevate your right leg to as close to vertical with the ground as you can make it making sure both knees are still slightly bent
3. Lower your right leg while raising your left leg to switch positions
4. Continue alternating leg position for an allotted time or repetitions

Exercise tips

While fatigue begins to settle into the core, the natural tendency will be to begin arching your lower back so that it comes off the floor or arching your neck. If this begins to occur you should immediately lower your legs back to the floor to reestablish proper form. You may also have the urge to place your hands underneath your hips to continue the exercise. This is a form of artificial strength that prevents your from accessing endurance and strength that can be acquired through keeping your palms on the floor by your sides.

 3x30 rep   **3x45 reps**   **3x60 reps**

Finding an exercise that allows you to maintain proper posture and spinal alignment while challenging the abdominal muscles is sometimes difficult to find. Continuously flexing and extending your spine, as you can witness in the standard crunch exercise, causes wear and tear on the spine. Allow yourself the benefit of strengthening your core while keeping your spine healthy by allowing it to remain in a optimal neutral position through an exercise known as flutter kicks.

Romanian twists

Preparation

a. Sit tall and upright on the flat surface with your knees bent and feet place shoulder-width apart.
b. Begin to take purposeful breaths by inhaling in through your nose and into your stomach while flexing your abdominal wall against the inhaled air. This will allow you to maintain a neutral spine throughout the exercise.
c. Lean your torso backwards to 30 to 45 degrees with the floor while elevating your heels 2 to 3 inches above the floor in order maintain your center of gravity.

The Exercise

1. Extend your arms and clasp your hands together in front of you chest or hold the medicine ball in front of your chest.

Keeping your core contracted and spine neutral and can now begin the exercise. To perform the romanian twist, you will now need to:

1. Begin to rotate your shoulders to the right keeping your hips stationary
2. Continue rotating to the furthest point which is allowing your hands or the medicine ball to touch the floor on the right side
3. Maintain a slow and controlled motion to rotate all the way to the left and again, touching the floor.
4. Continue alternating directions for an allotted time or repetitions.

Exercise tips

This exercise should not be performed to failure as you will inevitably begin to lose your proper spinal posture. Instead, stop the exercise before you cannot hold a neutral spine and continue to perform the exercise while increasing either the repetitions or the weight held in order to continuously build up your core strength. If using a medicine ball, you will need to keep your arms extended and the medicine ball in the middle of your chest throughout the exercise. This will add additional stress onto your arms and greatly progress the onset of fatigue.

| EASY | 3x30 rep | | MEDIUM | 3x45 reps | | HARD | 3x60 reps |

If you were to ask anybody frantically getting ready for beach season what the perfect beach body would consist of, you would irrefutably hear the words "6 pack abs." What many do not consider, however, is that your core is composed of muscles that wrap all the way around that besides for the obvious aesthetic appearance, need be trained to keep optimal posture and keep your spine healthy. This can all be accomplished through an exercise known as the romanian twist.

Toe touchers

Preparation

a. Lie your back onto the floor in an extended position.
b. Extend your legs with your knees slightly bent and your ankles flexed to 90 degrees.
c. Rotate your pelvis upward in order to keep your lower back flush with floor.
d. Maintain neutral spinal alignment by beginning to inhale through your nose and into your stomach while flexing your abdominal wall against the inhaled air.

The Exercise

1. Keeping your feet together as you raise your legs to become as vertical to the ground as possible
2. Extending your arms over your shoulders
3. Begin to raise your shoulders and upper back off the ground by flexing your lower ribcage into your belly button until you have reached your toes
4. Gently touch your toes before returning to the starting position and continue for the allotted repetitions

Exercise tips

If you are able to perform the toe toucher exercise with control and are needing to increase the difficulty you may implement dumbbells. This is done by grabbing a pair of dumbbells with a double overhand grip so that your palms are facing forward towards your legs. Perform the exercise by again flexing your lower ribcage into your belly button and extending the dumbbells up towards your toes. Once you've reached your toes, gently touch them with the dumbbells before exhaling and returning to the starting position.

 3x12 rep   3x15 reps   3x18 reps

In order to properly contract a muscle to force it to adapt and grow is by flexing the origin of the muscle into the insertion of the muscle. This becomes apparent when you perform a curl to flex your bicep. If your goal is to increase the aesthetic appearance of the front of your core you will need to perform the same action. This can be accomplished through an abdominal exercise known as toe touchers.